REGENTS PREPARATION, LLC

D0006287

-Presents-

ALGEBRA I

REGENTS EXAM
REVIEW MANUAL

WITH 9 REGENTS EXAMS,
7 TOPICALLY ORGANIZED

SPECIAL EDITION
Each Question Linked to a Solution Video
QR Coded for One to One Initiative

Production

235 1215225 10113519 1144 1015195168 192095812

Cover illustration by James A. Stiehl
Printed in the United States of America
ISBN: 978-0-578-19771-5

Algebra I
Table of Contents

POLYNOMIALS

1. Write the expression $5x + 4x^2(2x + 7) - 6x^2 - 9x$ as a polynomial in standard form.

08 2017 31

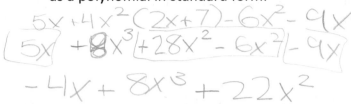

$$5x + 4x^2(2x+7) - 6x^2 - 9x$$
$$5x + 8x^3 + 28x^2 - 6x^2 - 9x$$
$$-4x + 8x^3 + 22x^2$$

2. Wenona sketched the polynomial $P(x)$ as shown on the axes below.

08 2017 07

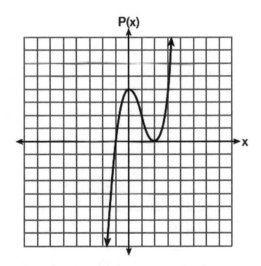

Which equation could represent $P(x)$?

1) $P(x) = (x + 1)(x - 2)^2$ 3) $P(x) = (x + 1)(x - 2)$

2) $P(x) = (x - 1)(x + 2)^2$ 4) $P(x) = (x - 1)(x + 2)$

3. The function *r(x)* is defined by the expression $x^2 + 3x - 18$. Use factoring to determine the zeros of *r(x)*.

    Explain what the zeros represent on the graph of *r(x)*.

    06 2017 33

4. If $f(x) = x^2$ and $g(x) = x$, determine the value(s) of *x* that satisfy the equation $f(x) = g(x)$.

    06 2017 31

5. Express in simplest form:
    $(3x^2 + 4x - 8) - (-2x^2 + 4x + 2)$

    06 2017 25

6. Which polynomial function has zeros at –3, 0, and 4?

    06 2017 10

    1) $f(x) = (x + 3)(x^2 + 4)$ 3) $f(x) = x(x + 3)(x - 4)$

    2) $f(x) = (x^2 - 3)(x - 4)$ 4) $f(x) = x(x - 3)(x + 4)$

7. Lynn, Jude, and Anne were given the
    Function $f(x) = -2x^2 + 32$, and they were
    asked to find $f(3)$. Lynn's answer was 14,
    Jude's answer was 4, and Anne's answer
    was ±4. Who is correct?

    06 2017 05

    1) Lynn, only   3) Anne, only

    2) Jude, only   4) Both Lynn and Jude

8. What is the product of $2x + 3$
    and $4x^2 - 5x + 6$?

    08 2016 12

    1) $8x^3 - 2x^2 + 3x + 18$
    2) $8x^3 - 2x^2 - 3x + 18$
    3) $8x^3 + 2x^2 - 3x + 18$
    4) $8x^3 + 2x^2 + 3x + 18$

9. When multiplying polynomials for a
    Math assignment, Pat found the
    product to be $-4x + 8x^2 - 2x^3 + 5$.
    He then had to state the leading
    coefficient of this polynomial.
    Pat wrote down −4. Do you agree with
    Pat's answer? Explain your reasoning.

    08 2016 28

10. The expression $x^4 - 16$ is equivalent to

   1) $(x^2 + 8)(x^2 - 8)$
   2) $(x^2 - 8)(x^2 - 8)$
   3) $(x^2 + 4)(x^2 - 4)$
   4) $(x^2 - 4)(x^2 - 4)$

11. An expression of the fifth degree is written with a leading coefficient of seven and a constant of six. Which expression is correctly written for these conditions?

   1) $6x^5 + x^4 + 7$
   2) $7x^6 - 6x^4 + 5$
   3) $6x^7 - x^5 + 5$
   4) $7x^5 + 2x^2 + 6$

12. The expression $3(x^2 - 1) - (x^2 - 7x + 10)$ is equivalent to

   1) $2x^2 - 7x + 7$
   2) $2x^2 + 7x - 13$
   3) $2x^2 - 7x + 9$
   4) $2x^2 + 7x - 11$

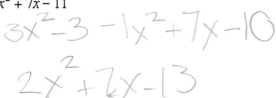

$$3x^2 - 3 - 1x^2 + 7x - 10$$
$$2x^2 + 2x - 13$$

13. Four expressions are shown below.

08 2015 09

I $2(2x^2 - 2x - 60)$

II $4(x^2 - x - 30)$

III $4(x + 6)(x - 5)$

IV $4x(x - 1) - 120$

The expression $4x^2 - 4x - 120$
is equivalent to

1)   I and II, only
2)   II and IV, only
3)   I, II, and IV
4)   II, III, and IV

14. Which trinomial is equivalent to
$3(x - 2)^2 - 2(x - 1)$?

08 2015 24

1) $3x^2 - 2x - 10$
2) $3x^2 - 2x - 14$
3) $3x^2 - 14x + 10$
4) $3x^2 - 14x + 14$

06 2015 28

15. If the difference $(3x^2 - 2x + 5) - (x^2 + 3x - 2)$
is multiplied by $\frac{1}{2}x^2$, what is the result,
written in standard form?

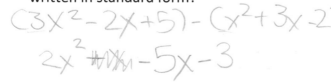

16. Fred is given a rectangular piece of paper. If the length of Fred's piece of paper is represented by $2x - 6$ and the width is represented by $3x - 5$, then the paper has a total area represented by

01 2015 10

1) $5x - 11$ 2) $6x^2 - 28x + 30$

3) $10x - 22$ 4) $6x^2 - 6x - 11$

$$2x - 6 \cdot 3x - 5$$
$$6x^2 + 30$$

17. Subtract $5x^2 + 2x - 11$ from $3x^2 + 8x - 7$. Express the result as a trinomial.

01 2015 28

$$(5x^2 + 2x - 11) - (3x^2 + 8x - 7)$$
$$2x^2 - 6x - 4$$

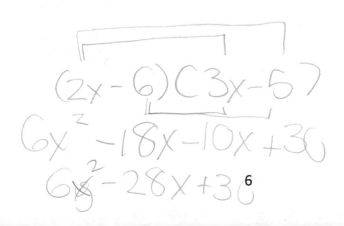

$$(2x - 6)(3x - 5)$$
$$6x^2 - 18x - 10x + 30$$
$$6x^2 - 28x + 30$$

6

PROPERTIES OF ALGEBRA

1. A two-inch-long grasshopper can jump a
    horizontal distance of 40 inches. An athlete,
    who is five feet nine, wants to cover a
    distance of one mile by jumping. If this
    person could jump at the same ratio of
    body-length to jump-length as the
    grasshopper, determine, to the *nearest
    jump*, how many jumps it would take this
    athlete to jump one mile.

    08 2017 30

    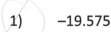

2. Using the formula for the volume of a cone,
    express *r* in terms of *V*, *h*, and π.

    08 2017 27

    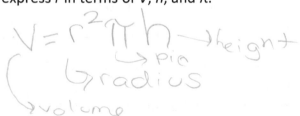

3. Which value of *x* satisfies the equation?

    08 2017 13

    $$\frac{5}{6}\left(\frac{3}{8} - x\right) = 16?$$

    1) −19.575   3)   −16.3125

    2) −18.825   4)   −15.6875

4. A part of Jennifer's work to solve the equation $2(6x^2 - 3) = 11x^2 - x$ is shown below.

    08 2017 01

    Given: $2(6x^2 - 3) = 11x^2 - x$
    Step 1: $12x^2 - 6 = 11x^2 - x$

    Which property justifies her first step?

    1) identity property of multiplication

    3) commutative property of multiplication

    2) multiplication property of equality

    4) distributive property of multiplication over subtraction

5. The formula for blood flow rate is given by $F = \dfrac{P_1 - P_2}{r}$, where F is the flow rate, P_1 the initial pressure, P_2 the final pressure, and r the resistance created by blood vessel size. Which formula can *not* be derived from the given formula?

    06 2017 23

    1) $P_1 = Fr + P_2$

    3) $r = F(P_2 - P_1)$

    2) $P_2 = P_1 - Fr$

    4) $r = \dfrac{P_1 - P_2}{F}$

6. An equation is given below.

06 2017 19

$$4(x - 7) = 0.3(x + 2) + 2.11$$

The solution to the equation is

1) 8.3   3) 3

2) 8.7   4) −3

7. The formula for the surface area of a right rectangular prism is $A = 2lw + 2hw + 2lh$, where *l*, *w*, and *h* represent the length, width, and height, respectively. Which term of this formula is *not* dependent on the height?

06 2017 02

1) *A*   3) $2hw$

2) $2lw$ 4) $2lh$

8. Solve the equation below for *x* in terms of *a*. $4(ax + 3) - 3ax = 25 + 3a$

08 2016 32

9. The formula for the sum of the degree measures of the interior angles of a polygon is $S = 180(n - 2)$. Solve for n, the number of sides of the polygon, in terms of S.

06 2016 31

10. The volume of a large can of tuna fish can be calculated using the formula $V = \pi r^2 h$. Write an equation to find the radius, r, in terms of V and h. Determine the diameter, to the nearest inch, of a large can of tuna fish that has a volume of 66 cubic inches and a height of 3.3 inches.

08 2015 35

11. The distance a free falling object has traveled can be modeled by the equation $d = \frac{1}{2} at^2$, where a is acceleration due to gravity and t is the amount of time the object has fallen. What is t in terms of a and d?

06 2015 19

1) $t = \sqrt{\dfrac{da}{2}}$

2) $t = \sqrt{\dfrac{2d}{a}}$

3) $t = \left(\dfrac{da}{d}\right)^2$

4) $t = \left(\dfrac{2d}{a}\right)^2$

12. A student is asked to solve the equation $4(3x-1)^2 - 17 = 83$. The student's solution to the problem starts as $4(3x-1)^2 = 100$

$$(3x-1)^2 = 25$$

06 2015 21

A correct next step in the solution of the problem is

1) $3x - 1 = \pm 5$ 2) $3x - 1 = \pm 25$

3) $9x^2 - 1 = 25$ 4) $9x^2 - 6x + 1 = 5$

13. Peyton is a sprinter who can run the 40-yard dash in 4.5 seconds. He converts his speed into miles per hour, as shown below.

01 2015 02

$$\frac{40 \text{ yd}}{4.5 \text{ sec}} \cdot \frac{3 \text{ ft}}{1 \text{ yd}} \cdot \frac{5280 \text{ ft}}{1 \text{ mi}} \cdot \frac{60 \text{ sec}}{1 \text{ min}} \cdot \frac{60 \text{ min}}{1 \text{ hr}}$$

Which ratio is *incorrectly* written to convert his speed?

1) $\dfrac{3 \text{ ft}}{1 \text{ yd}}$ 2) $\dfrac{5280 \text{ ft}}{1 \text{ mi}}$

3) $\dfrac{60 \text{ sec}}{1 \text{ min}}$ 4) $\dfrac{60 \text{ min}}{1 \text{ hr}}$

14. The equation for the volume of a cylinder is $V = \pi r^2 h$. The positive value of r, in terms of h and V, is

01 2015 16

1) $r = \sqrt{\dfrac{V}{\pi h}}$ 2) $r = \sqrt{V \pi h}$

3) $r = 2V\pi h$ 4) $r = \dfrac{V}{2\pi}$

15. An astronaut drops a rock off the edge of a cliff on the Moon. The distance, $d(t)$, in meters, the rock travels after t seconds can be modeled by the function $d(t) = 0.8t^2$.

01 2015 21

What is the average speed, in meters per second, of the rock between 5 and 10 seconds after it was dropped?

1) 12

2) 20

3) 60

4) 80

16. The school newspaper surveyed the student body for an article about club membership. The table below shows the number of students in each grade level who belong to one or more clubs.

01 2015 26

	1 Club	2 Clubs	3 or More Clubs
9th	90	33	12
10th	125	12	15
11th	87	22	18
12th	75	27	23

If there are 180 students in ninth grade, what percentage of the ninth grade students belong to more than one club?

FUNCTIONS

1. The zeros of the function
   $f(x) = 2x^3 + 12x - 10x^2$ are

   08 2017 19

   1) $\{2, 3\}$ 3) $\{0, 2, 3\}$

   2) $\{-1, 6\}$ 4) $\{0, -1, 6\}$

2. The highest possible grade for a book
   report is 100. The teacher deducts 10
   points for each day the report is late.
   Which kind of function describes
   this situation?

   08 2017 17

   1) linear   3) exponential growth

   2) quadratic   4) exponential decay

3. What is the domain of the relation
   shown below?

   08 2017 10

   $\{(4, 2), (1, 1), (0, 0), (1, -1), (4, -2)\}$

   1) $\{0, 1, 4\}$ 3) $\{-2, -1, 0, 1, 2, 4\}$

   2) $\{-2, -1, 0, 1, 2\}$ 4) $\{-2, -1, 0, 0, 1, 1, 1, 2, 4, 4\}$

4. The graph below models the height of a remote-control helicopter over 20 seconds during flight.

08 2017 05

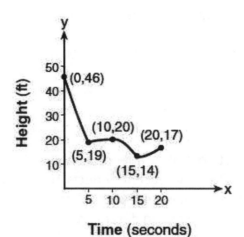

Over which interval does the helicopter have the *slowest* average rate of change?

1)   0 to 5 seconds

3) 10 to 15 seconds

2)   5 to 10 seconds

4) 15 to 20 seconds

5.   If $f(x) = \frac{1}{2}x^2 - \left(\frac{1}{4}x + 3\right)$, what is the value of $f(8)$?

08 2017 04

1) 11

3) 27

2) 17

4) 33

6. Which value of x results in equal outputs for
    $j(x) = 3x - 2$ and $b(x) = |x + 2|$?

    08 2017 02

    1) −2   3) $\frac{2}{3}$

    2) 2   4) 4

7. Given: $g(x) = 2x^2 + 3x + 10$

    06 2017 35

    $k(x) = 2x + 16$

    Solve the equation $g(x) = 2k(x)$ algebraically for x, to the *nearest tenth*.

    Explain why you chose the method you used to solve this quadratic equation.

8. Describe the effect that each transformation below has on the function $f(x) = |x|$, where $a > 0$.

    06 2017 32

    $g(x) = |x - a|$
    $h(x) = |x| - a$

9. Morgan throws a ball up into the air. The height of the ball above the ground, in feet, is modeled by the function $h(t) = -16t^2 + 24t$, where t represents the time, in seconds, since the ball was thrown. What is the appropriate domain for this situation?

    06 2017 24

    1) $0 \le t \le 1.5$

    3) $0 \le h(t) \le 1.5$

    2) $0 \le t \le 9$

    4) $0 \le h(t) \le 9$

10. One characteristic of all linear functions is that they change by

    06 2017 21

    1) equal factors over equal intervals

    3) equal differences over equal intervals

    2) unequal factors over equal intervals

    4) unequal differences over equal intervals

11. Which statement is true about the quadratic functions $g(x)$, shown in the table below, and $f(x) = (x - 3)^2 + 2$?

06 2017 17

x	g(x)
0	4
1	–1
2	–4
3	–5
4	–4
5	–1
6	4

1) They have the same vertex.

3) They have the same axis of symmetry.

2) They have the same zeros.

4) They intersect at two points.

12. A mapping is shown in the diagram below.

06 2017 09

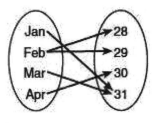

This mapping is

1) a function, because Feb has two outputs, 28 and 29

3) not a function, because Feb has two outputs, 28 and 29

2) a function, because two inputs, Jan and Mar, result in the output 31

4) not a function, because two inputs, Jan and Mar, result in the output 31

13.   The graph below shows the distance in
miles, *m*, hiked from a camp in *h* hours.

08 2016 01

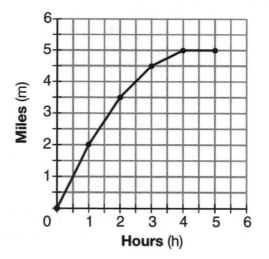

Which hourly interval had the greatest rate
of change?

1) hour 0 to hour 1
2) hour 1 to hour 2
3) hour 2 to hour 3
4) hour 3 to hour 4

14. Which chart could represent the function $f(x) = -2x + 6$?

08 2016 04

1)

x	f(x)
0	6
2	10
4	14
6	18

2)

x	f(x)
0	4
2	6
4	8
6	10

3)

x	f(x)
0	8
2	10
4	12
6	14

4)

x	f(x)
0	6
2	2
4	-2
6	-6

15. If $f(n) = (n - 1)^2 + 3n$,
which statement is true?

08 2016 05

1) $f(3) = -2$ 2) $f(-2) = 3$

3) $f(-2) = -15$ 4) $f(-15) = -2$

16. Which function has a constant rate of change equal to -3?

08 2016 15

1)

x	y
0	2
1	5
2	8
3	11

2) $\{(1,5),(2,2),(3,-5),(4,4)\}$

3)

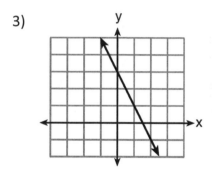

4) $2y = -6x + 10$

17. As *x* increases beyond 25, which function will have the largest value?

08 2016 18

1) $f(x) = 1.5^x$

2) $g(x) = 1.5x + 3$

3) $h(x) = 1.5x^2$

4) $k(x) = 1.5x^3 + 1.5x^2$

18. An online company lets you download songs for $0.99 each after you have paid a $5 membership fee. Which domain would be most appropriate to calculate the cost to download songs?

08 2016 20

1) rational numbers greater than zero
2) whole numbers greater than or equal to one
3) integers less than or equal to zero
4) whole numbers less than or equal to one

19. Richard is asked to transform the graph of $b(x)$ below.

08 2016 26

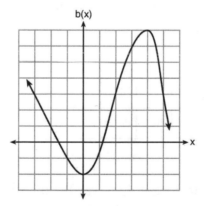

b(x)

The graph of $b(x)$ is transformed using the equation $h(x) = b(x - 2) - 3$. Describe how the graph of $b(x)$ changed to form the graph of $h(x)$.

20. The graph below shows two functions, $f(x)$ and $g(x)$. State all the values of x for which $f(x) = g(x)$.

08 2016 30

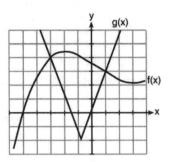

21. The table below shows the year and the number of households in a building that had high-speed broadband internet access.

06 2016 03

Number of Households	11	16	23	33	42	47
Year	2002	2003	2004	2005	2006	2007

For which interval of time was the average rate of change the *smallest*?

1) 2002 – 2004   2) 2003 - 2005

3) 2004 – 2006   4) 2005 - 2007

22

22.   The tables below show the values of four
        different functions for given values of *x*.

06 2016 06

x	f(x)
1	12
2	19
3	26
4	33

x	g(x)
1	-1
2	1
3	5
4	13

x	h(x)
1	9
2	12
3	17
4	24

x	k(x)
1	-2
2	4
3	14
4	28

Which table represents a linear function?·

1)   *f(x)*   2)   *g(x)*

3)   *h(x)*   4)   *k(x)*

23.   The range of the function
        $f(x) = x^2 + 2x - 8$ is all real numbers

06 2016 11

1) less than or equal to -9
2) greater than or equal to -9
3) less than or equal to -1
4) greater than or equal to -1

24.   The zeros of the function $f(x) = x^2 - 5x - 6$
        are

06 2016 12

1) -1 and 6   2)   1 and -6

3)   2 and -3 4) -2 and 3

25.   A store sells self-serve frozen yogurt sundaes.   **06 2016 23**
        The function $C(w)$ represents the cost, in
        dollars, of a sundae weighing w ounces.
        An appropriate domain for the function
        would be

        1) integers
        2) rational numbers
        3) nonnegative integers
        4) nonnegative rational numbers

                                                            06 2016 25

26.   Given that $f(x) = 2x + 1$, find $g(x)$
        if $g(x) = 2[f(x)]^2 - 1$.

27.   In the diagram below, $f(x) = x^3 + 2x^2$ is
        graphed. Also graphed is $g(x)$, the result
        of a translation of $f(x)$.

                                                            06 2016 32

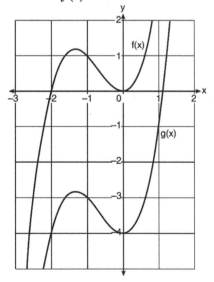

        Determine an equation of $g(x)$.   Explain your reasoning.

28.   The graph of $f(x)$ is shown below.   08 2015 04

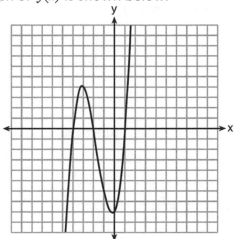

Which function could represent the
graph of $f(x)$?

1) $f(x) = (x + 2)(x^2 + 3x - 4)$ 2) $f(x) = (x - 2)(x^2 + 3x - 4)$

3) $f(x) = (x + 2)(x^2 + 3x + 4)$ 4) $f(x) = (x - 2)(x^2 + 3x + 4)$

29.   Which representations are functions?   08 2015 11

I

x	y
2	6
3	-12
4	7
5	5
2	-6

III

II $\{ (1,1), (2,1), (3,2), (4,3), (5,5), (6,8), (7,13) \}$ IV $y = 2x + 1$

1)   I and II   2)   II and IV

3)   III, only   4)   IV, only

25

30.　　If $f(x) = \dfrac{\sqrt{2x+3}}{6x-5}$, then $f\left(\dfrac{1}{2}\right) =$

08 2015 12

1)　　1　　　　　　2)　　-2

3)　　−1　　　　　4)　　$-\dfrac{13}{3}$

31.　　Which table represents a function?

06 2015 04

1)

x	2	4	2	4
f(x)	3	5	7	9

2)

x	0	−1	0	1
f(x)	0	1	−1	0

3)

x	3	5	7	9
f(x)	2	4	2	4

4)

x	0	1	−1	0
f(x)	0	−1	0	1

32.　　The graph of the function $f(x) = \sqrt{x+4}$ is shown below.

06 2015 09

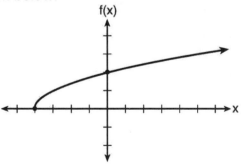

The domain of the function is

1) $\{x|x > 0\}$　　　　　　2) $\{x|x \geq 0\}$

3) $\{x|x > -4\}$　　　　　4) $\{x|x \geq -4\}$

33. If $f(x) = 3^x$ and $g(x) = 2x + 5$, at which value of x is $f(x) < g(x)$?

06 2015 15

1) –1
2) 2
3) –3
4) 4

34. The equation to determine the weekly earnings of an employee at The Hamburger Shack is given by $w(x)$, where x is the number of hours worked.

06 2015 34

$$w(x) = \begin{cases} 10x, & 0 \le x \le 40 \\ 15(x - 40) + 400, & x > 40 \end{cases}$$

Determine the difference in salary, *in dollars*, for an employee who works 52 hours versus one who works 38 hours. Determine the number of hours an employee must work in order to earn $445. Explain how you arrived at this answer.

35.   A function is shown in the table below.   01 2015 27

x	f(x)
–4	2
–1	–4
0	–2
3	16

If included in the table, which ordered pair, $(-4,1)$ or $(1,-4)$, would result in a relation that is no longer a function? Explain your answer.

36.   Graph the following function on the set   01 2015 30
of axes below.

$$f(x) = \begin{cases} |x|, & -3 \le x < 1 \\ 4, & 1 \le x \le 8 \end{cases}$$

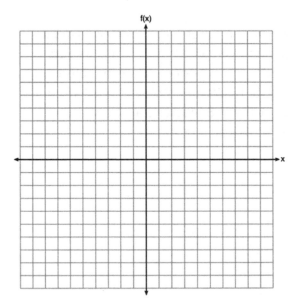

CREATING AND INTERPRETING EQUATIONS

1. Zeke and six of his friends are going to a
    baseball game. Their combined money
    totals $28.50. At the game, hot dogs cost
    $1.25 each, hamburgers cost $2.50 each,
    and sodas cost $0.50 each.
    Each person buys one soda.
    They spend all $28.50 on food and soda.
    Write an equation that can determine the
    number of hot dogs, *x*, and hamburgers, *y*,
    Zeke and his friends can buy.
    Graph your equation on the grid below.

    08 2017 37

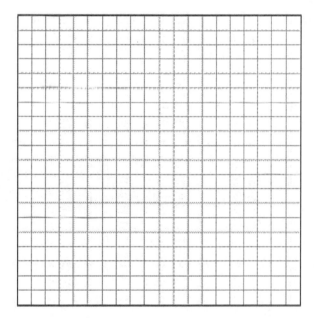

Determine how many different combinations,
including those combinations containing zero, of hot dogs
and hamburgers Zeke and his friends can buy, spending
all $28.50. Explain your answer.

2. Loretta and her family are going on vacation. **08 2017 33**
    Their destination is 610 miles from their
    home. Loretta is going to share some of
    the driving with her dad. Her average
    speed while driving is 55 mph and her
    dad's average speed while driving is 65 mph.
    The plan is for Loretta to drive
    for the first 4 hours of the trip and her dad to
    drive for the remainder of the trip. Determine
    the number of hours it will take her family to
    reach their destination. After Loretta has been
    driving for 2 hours, she gets tired and asks her
    dad to take over.

    Determine, to the *nearest tenth of an hour*, how much
    time the family will save by having Loretta's dad drive for
    the remainder of the trip.

3. Abigail's and Gina's ages are consecutive **08 2017 23**
    integers. Abigail is younger than Gina
    and Gina's age is represented by *x*.
    If the difference of the square of Gina's
    age and eight times Abigail's age is 17,
    which equation could be used to find
    Gina's age?

    1) $(x+1)^2 - 8x = 17$ 3) $x^2 - 8(x+1) = 17$

    2) $(x-1)^2 - 8x = 17$ 4) $x^2 - 8(x-1) = 17$

4.   A plumber has a set fee for a house call
and charges by the hour for repairs. The
total cost of her services can be modeled
by $c(t) = 125t + 95$. Which statements
about this function are true?

08 2017 09

I.   A house call fee costs $95.
II.   The plumber charges $125 per hour.
III.   The number of hours the job takes is
        represented by *t*.

1) I and II, only   3) II and III, only

2) I and III, only   4) I, II, and III

5.   The value, $v(t)$, of a car depreciates according
to the function $v(t) = P(.85)^t$, where *P* is the
purchase price of the car and *t* is the time,
in years, since the car was purchased.
State the percent that the value of the
car *decreases* by each year.

06 2017 28

Justify your answer.

6.   A student plotted the data from a sleep
       study as shown in the graph below.

06 2017 04

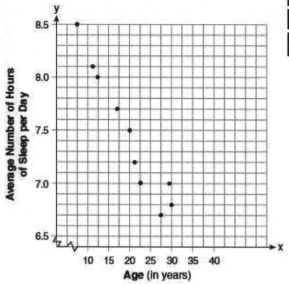

The student used the equation of the line
$y = -0.09x + 9.24$ to model the data. What does the rate
of change represent in terms of these data?

1) The average number of
   hours of sleep per day
   increases 0.09 hour per
   year of age.

3) The average number of
   hours of sleep per day
   increases 9.24 hours per
   year of age.

2) The average number of
   hours of sleep per day
   decreases 0.09 hour per
   year of age.

4) The average number of
   hours of sleep per day
   decreases 9.24 hours per
   year of age.

7.   A parking garage charges a base rate of $3.50   08 2016 14
up to 2 hours, and an hourly rate for each
additional hour. The sign below gives the
prices for up to 5 hours of parking.

Parking Rates	
2 hours	$3.50
3 hours	$9.00
4 hours	$14.50
5 hours	$20.00

Which linear equation can be used to find *x*,
the additional hourly parking rate?

1) $9.00 + 3x = 20.00$
2) $9.00 + 3.50x = 20.00$
3) $2x + 3.50 = 14.50$
4) $2x + 9.00 = 14.50$

8.   Kendal bought *x* boxes of cookies to bring to   08 2016 16
a party. Each box contains 12 cookies.
She decides to keep two boxes for herself.
She brings 60 cookies to the party. Which
equation can be used to find the number of
boxes, *x*, Kendal bought?

1) $2x - 12 = 60$
2) $12x - 2 = 60$
3) $12x - 24 = 60$
4) $24 - 12x = 60$

9.   Sara was asked to solve this word problem: 06 2016 24
       "The product of two consecutive integers is
       156. What are the integers?" What type of
       equation should she create to solve
       this problem?

       1)   linear
       2)   quadratic
       3)   exponential
       4)   absolute value

10.   Sue and Kathy were doing their algebra   06 2016 29
       homework. They were asked to write
       the equation of the line that passes through
       the points $(-3, 4)$ and $(6, 1)$.

       Sue wrote $y - 4 = -\frac{1}{3}(x + 3)$ and Kathy wrote

       $y = -\frac{1}{3}x + 3$. Justify why both students are correct.

11.   During a recent snowstorm in Red Hook,   06 2016 30
       NY, Jaime noted that there were 4 inches
       of snow on the ground at 3:00 p.m., and
       there were 6 inches of snow on the ground
       at 7:00 p.m. If she were to graph these data,
       what does the slope of the line connecting
       these two points represent in the context of
       this problem?

12.   An airplane leaves New York City and heads   06 2016 35
toward Los Angeles. As it climbs, the plane
gradually increases its speed until it reaches
cruising altitude, at which time it maintains a
constant speed for several hours as long as it
stays at cruising altitude. After flying for 32
minutes, the plane reaches cruising altitude
and has flown 192 miles. After flying for a
total of 92 minutes, the plane has flown a
total of 762 miles. Determine the speed
of the plane, at cruising altitude, in miles per
minute. Write an equation to represent
the number of miles the plane has flown,
y, during x minutes at cruising altitude, only.
Assuming that the plane maintains its
speed at cruising altitude, determine the total
number of miles the plane has flown 2 hours
into the flight.

13.   Rowan has $50 in a savings jar and is putting in   08 2015 02
$5 every week. Jonah has $10 in his own jar
and is putting in $15 every week. Each of
them plots his progress on a graph with time
on the horizontal axis and amount in the jar
on the vertical axis. Which statement about
their graphs is true?

1) Rowan's graph has a steeper slope than
Jonah's.
2) Rowan's graph always lies above Jonah's.
3) Jonah's graph has a steeper slope than
Rowan's.
4) Jonah's graph always lies above Rowan's.

14. To watch a varsity basketball game, spectators must buy a ticket at the door. The cost of an adult ticket is $3.00 and the cost of a student ticket is $1.50. If the number of adult tickets sold is represented by a and student tickets sold by s, which expression represents the amount of money collected at the door from the ticket sales?

08 2015 03

   1) $4.50as$
   2) $4.50(a + s)$
   3) $(3.00a)(1.50s)$
   4) $3.00a + 1.50s$

15. A typical cell phone plan has a fixed base fee that includes a certain amount of data and an overage charge for data use beyond the plan. A cell phone plan charges a base fee of $62 and an overage charge of $30 per gigabyte of data that exceed 2 gigabytes. If C represents the cost and g represents the total number of gigabytes of data, which equation could represent this plan when more than 2 gigabytes are used?

08 2015 08

   1) $C = 30 + 62(2 - g)$ 2) $C = 30 + 62(g - 2)$

   3) $C = 62 + 30(2 - g)$ 4) $C = 62 + 30(g - 2)$

16. Firing a piece of pottery in a kiln takes place at different temperatures for different amounts of time. The graph below shows the temperatures in a kiln while firing a piece of pottery after the kiln is preheated to 200ºF.

08 2015 15

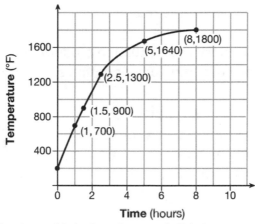

Time (hours)

During which time interval did the temperature in the kiln show the greatest average rate of change?

1) 0 to 1 hour

2) 1 hour to 1.5 hours

3) 2.5 hours to 5 hours

4) 5 hours to 8 hours

17. The cost of airing a commercial on television is modeled by the function $C(n) = 110n + 900$, where *n* is the number of times the commercial is aired. Based on this model, which statement is true?

06 2015 01

1) The commercial costs $0 to produce and $110 per airing up to $900.

2) The commercial costs $110 to produce and $900 each time it is aired.

3) The commercial costs $900 to produce and $110 each time it is aired.

4) The commercial costs $1010 to produce and can air an unlimited number of times.

18. The function $V(t) = 1350(1.017)^t$ represents the value $V(t)$, in dollars, of a comic book t years after its purchase. The yearly rate of appreciation of the comic book is

06 2015 17

1) 17%
2) 1.7%
3) 1.017%
4) 0.017%

19. Alex is selling tickets to a school play. An adult ticket costs $6.50 and a student ticket costs $4.00. Alex sells x adult tickets and student tickets. Write a function, $f(x)$, to represent how much money Alex collected from selling tickets.

06 2015 26

20. Dylan invested $600 in a savings account at a 1.6% annual interest rate. He made no deposits or withdrawals on the account for 2 years. The interest was compounded annually. Find, to the *nearest cent*, the balance in the account after 2 years.

06 2015 29

21. The owner of a small computer repair business has one employee, who is paid an hourly rate of $22. The owner estimates his weekly profit using the function $P(x) = 8600 - 22x$. In this function, x represents the number of

01 2015 01

   1) computers repaired per week
   2) hours worked per week
   3) customers served per week
   4) days worked per week

22. In 2013, the United States Postal Service charged $0.46 to mail a letter weighing up to 1 oz. and $0.20 per ounce for each additional ounce. Which function would determine the cost, in dollars, $c(z)$, of mailing a letter weighing z ounces where z is an integer greater than 1?

01 2015 23

   1) $c(z) = 0.46z + 0.20$
   2) $c(z) = 0.20z + 0.46$
   3) $c(z) = 0.46(z - 1) + 0.20$
   4) $c(z) = 0.20(z - 1) + 0.46$

23.   A gardener is planting two types of trees: 01 2015 31
Type *A* is three feet tall and grows at a rate
of 15 inches per year. Type *B* is four feet tall

and grows at a rate of 10 inches per year.
Algebraically determine exactly how many
years it will take for these trees to be the
same height.

24.   New Clarendon Park is undergoing   01 2015 37
renovations to its gardens. One garden that
was originally a square is being adjusted so

that one side is doubled in length, while
the other side is decreased by three
meters. The new rectangular garden will
have an area that is 25% more than the
original square garden. Write an equation
that could be used to determine the length
of a side of the original square garden.
Explain how your equation models the
situation. Determine the area, in square
meters, of the new rectangular garden.

INEQUALITIES

1. Solve the following system of inequalities graphically on the grid below and label the solution *S*.

08 2017 35

$$3x + 4y > 20$$

$$x < 3y - 18$$

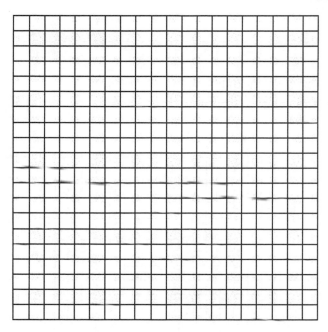

Is the point $(3, 7)$ in the solution set? Explain your answer.

2.	What is the solution to the inequality

$$2 + \frac{4}{9}x \geq 4 + x?$$

08 2017 11

1) $x \leq -\frac{18}{5}$

3) $x \leq \frac{54}{5}$

2) $x \geq -\frac{18}{5}$

4) $x \geq \frac{54}{5}$

3.	Graph the inequality $y + 4 < -2(x - 4)$ on the set of axes below.

06 2017 30

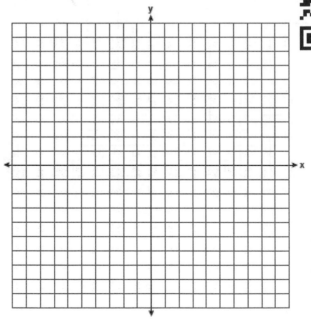

4. Which value would be a solution for *x* in the inequality $47 - 4x < 7$?

06 2017 13

1) −13

3) 10

2) −10

4) 11

5. Jordan works for a landscape company during his summer vacation. He is paid $12 per hour for mowing lawns and $14 per hour for planting gardens. He can work a maximum of 40 hours per week, and would like to earn at least $250 this week. If *m* represents the number of hours mowing lawns and *g* represents the number of hours planting gardens, which system of inequalities could be used to represent the given conditions?

06 2017 11

1) $m + g \le 40$
   $12m + 14g \ge 250$

3) $m + g \le 40$
   $12m + 14g \le 250$

2) $m + g \ge 40$
   $12m + 14g \le 250$

4) $m + g \ge 40$
   $12m + 14g \ge 250$

6. What is the solution to $2h + 8 > 3h - 6$

08 2016 07

1) $h < 14$
2) $h < \dfrac{14}{5}$
3) $h > 14$
4) $h > \dfrac{14}{5}$

7. Shawn incorrectly graphed the inequality $-x - 2y \geq 8$ as shown below.

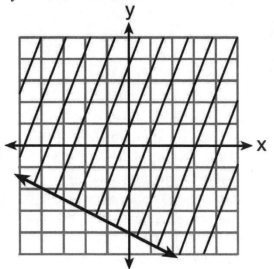

Explain Shawn's mistake. Graph the inequality correctly on the set of axes below.

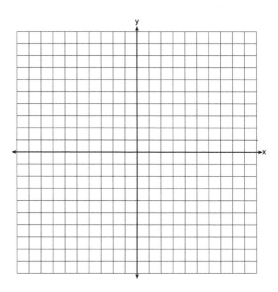

8. The acidity in a swimming pool is considered normal if the average of three pH readings, *p*, is defined such that $7.0 < p < 7.8$. If the first two readings are 7.2 and 7.6, which value for the third reading will result in an overall rating of normal?

06 2016 07

1) 6.2
2) 7.3
3) 8.6
4) 8.8

9. When $3x + 2 \leq 5(x - 4)$ is solved for *x*, the solution is

06 2016 09

1) $x \leq 3$
2) $x \geq 3$
3) $x \leq -11$
4) $x \geq 11$

10. What is the largest integer, *x*, for which the value of $f(x) = 5x^4 + 30x^2 + 9$ will be greater than the value of $g(x) = 3^x$?

06 2016 21

1) 7
2) 8
3) 9
4) 10

11.   The cost of a pack of chewing gum   08 2015 05
in a vending machine is $0.75. The cost
of a bottle of juice in the same machine
is $1.25. Julia has $22.00 to spend on
chewing gum and bottles of juice for her
team and she must buy seven packs of
chewing gum. If *b* represents the number
of bottles of juice, which inequality represents
the maximum number of bottles she can buy?

1) $0.75b + 1.25(7) \geq 22$

2) $0.75b + 1.25(7) \leq 22$

3) $0.75(7) + 1.25b \geq 22$

4) $0.75(7) + 1.25b \leq 22$

12.   Which graph represents the solution of   08 2015 06
$y \leq x + 3$ and $y \geq -2x - 2$?

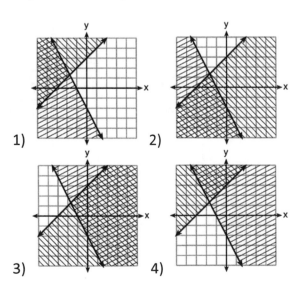

1)

2)

3)

4)

13.   On the set of axes below,   **08 2015 26**
       graph the inequality $2x + y > 1$

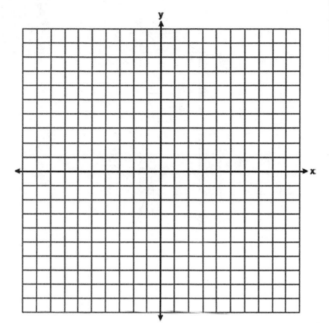

14.   Solve for *x* algebraically: **08 2015 34**
       $7x - 3(4x - 8) \leq 6x + 12 - 9x$
       If *x* is a number in the interval $[4, 8]$,
       state all integers that satisfy the given
       inequality.

       Explain how you determined these values.

15. Which inequality is represented in the graph below?

06 2015 05

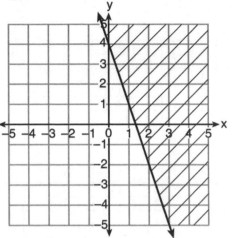

1) $y \geq -3x + 4$

2) $y \leq -3x + 4$

3) $y \geq -4x - 3$

4) $y \leq -4x - 3$

16. Natasha is planning a school celebration and wants to have live music and food for everyone who attends. She has found a band that will charge her $750 and a caterer who will provide snacks and drinks for $2.25 per person. If her goal is to keep the average cost per person between $2.75 and $3.25, how many people, *p*, must attend?

06 2015 24

1) $225 < p < 325$

2) $325 < p < 750$

3) $500 < p < 1000$

4) $750 < p < 1500$

17. Determine the smallest integer that makes
$-3x + 7 - 5x < 15$ true.

06 2015 30

18. An on-line electronics store must sell at
least $2500 worth of printers and
computers per day. Each printer costs
$50 and each computer costs $500.
The store can ship a maximum of 15
items per day. On the set of axes below,
graph a system of inequalities that models
these constraints.

06 2015 35

Number of Computers

Number of Printers

Determine a combination of printers and computers that
would allow the electronics store to meet all of the
constraints. Explain how you obtained your answer.

19. The inequality $7 - \frac{2}{3}x < x - 8$

is equivalent to

01 2015 07

1) $x > 9$

2) $x > -\frac{3}{5}$

3) $x < 9$

4) $x < -\frac{3}{5}$

20. Connor wants to attend the town carnival. The price of admission to the carnival is $4.50, and each ride costs an additional 79 cents. If he can spend at most $16.00 at the carnival, which inequality can be used to solve for r, the number of rides Connor can go on, and what is the maximum number of rides he can go on?

01 2015 13

1) $0.79 + 4.50r \leq 16.00$; 3 rides
2) $0.79 + 4.50r \leq 16.00$; 4 rides
3) $4.50 + 0.79r \leq 16.00$; 14 rides
4) $4.50 + 0.79r \leq 16.00$; 15 rides

21.   The graph of an inequality is shown below.

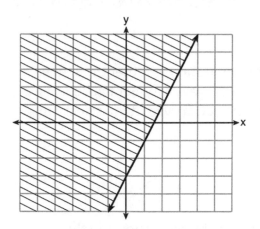

a) Write the inequality represented by the graph.

b) On the same set of axes, graph the inequality
   $x + 2y < 4$.

c) The two inequalities graphed on the set of axes form a system. Oscar thinks that the point $(2,1)$ is in the solution set for this system of inequalities.

Determine and state whether you agree with Oscar. Explain your reasoning

SEQUENCES AND SERIES

1. Determine and state whether the sequence $1, 3, 9, 27, \ldots$ displays exponential behavior. Explain how you arrived at your decision.

08 2017 26

2. A sequence of blocks is shown in the diagram below.

08 2017 15

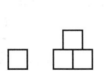

This sequence can be defined by the recursive function $a_1 = 1$ and $a_n = a_{n-1} + n$. Assuming the pattern continues, how many blocks will there be when $n = 7$?

1) 13

3) 28

2) 21

4) 36

3.   Given the function $f(n)$ defined by
      the following:

06 2017 18

$$f(1) = 2$$
$$f(n) = -5f(n-1) + 2$$

Which set could represent the range of
the function?

1) $\{2, 4, 6, 8, \ldots\}$ 3) $\{-8, -42, -208, 1042, \ldots\}$

2) $\{2, -8, 42, -208, \ldots\}$ 4) $\{-10, 50, -250, 1250, \ldots\}$

4.   Which function defines the sequence
      $-6, -10, -14, -18, \ldots$, where $f(6) = -26$?

08 2016 10

1) $f(x) = -4x - 2$
2) $f(x) = 4x - 2$
3) $f(x) = -x + 32$
4) $f(x) = x - 26$

5.   In a sequence, the first term is 4 and the
      common difference is 3. The fifth term
      of this sequence is

06 2016 13

1) -11
2) -8
3) 16
4) 19

6. Which recursively defined function has a first term equal to 10 and a common difference of 4?

08 2015 14

1) $f(1) = 10$

$f(x) = f(x-1) + 4$

2) $f(1) = 4$

$f(x) = f(x-1) + 10$

3) $f(1) = 10$

$f(x) = 4f(x-1)$

4) $f(1) = 4$

$f(x) = 10f(x-1)$

7. Alicia has invented a new app for smart phones that two companies are interested in purchasing for a 2-year contract. Company *A* is offering her $10,000 for the first month and will increase the amount each month by $5000. Company *B* is offering $500 for the first month and will double their payment each month from the previous month. Monthly payments are made at the end of each month.
For which monthly payment will company *B*'s payment first exceed company *A*'s payment?

08 2015 18

1) 6

2) 7

3) 8

4) 9

8.   Each day Toni records the height of a plant   08 2015 25
for her science lab. Her data are shown in
the table below.

Day (n)	1	2	3	4	5
Height (cm)	3.0	4.5	6.0	7.5	9.0

The plant continues to grow at a constant
daily rate. Write an equation to represent
$h(n)$, the height of the plant on the nth day.

9.   Jackson is starting an exercise program.   08 2015 32
The first day he will spend 30 minutes on
a treadmill. He will increase his time on
the treadmill by 2 minutes each day.
Write an equation for $T(d)$, the time, in
minutes, on the treadmill on day d.
Find $T(6)$, the minutes he will spend on
the treadmill on day 6.

10.   A pattern of blocks is shown below.   06 2015 22

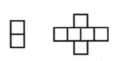

Term 1   Term 2   Term 3   Term 4

If the pattern of blocks continues, which formula(s) could be used to determine the number of blocks in the *n*th   term?

I	II	III
$a_n = n + 4$	$a_1 = 2$ $a_n = a_{n-1} + 4$	$a_n = 4n - 2$

1) I and II
2) I and III
3) II and III
4) III, only

11.   If a sequence is defined recursively by $f(0) = 2$ and $f(n + 1) = -2f(n) + 3$ for $n \geq 0$, then $f(2)$ is equal to   01 2015 20

1) 1
2) −11
3) 5
4) 17

SYSTEMS OF EQUATIONS

1. The graph below models the cost of renting video games with a membership in Plan *A* and Plan *B*.

    08 2017 28

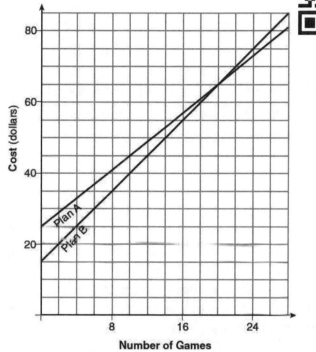

Explain why Plan *B* is the better choice for Dylan if he only has $50 to spend on video games, including a membership fee. Bobby wants to spend $65 on video games, including a membership fee.

Which plan should he choose?

Explain your answer.

2.   Which system of equations does *not* have the same solution as the system below?

08 2017 24

$$4x + 3y = 10$$
$$-6x - 5y = -16$$

1) $-12x - 9y = -30$
    $12x + 10y = 32$

3) $24x + 18y = 60$
    $-24x - 20y = -64$

2) $20x + 15y = 50$
    $-18x - 15y = -48$

4) $40x + 30y = 100$
    $36x + 30y = -96$

3.   Central High School had five members on their swim team in 2010. Over the next several years, the team increased by an average of 10 members per year. The same school had 35 members in their chorus in 2010. The chorus saw an increase of 5 members per year.

06 2017 37

Write a system of equations to model this situation, where *x* represents the number of years since 2010.

Graph this system of equations on the set of axes below.

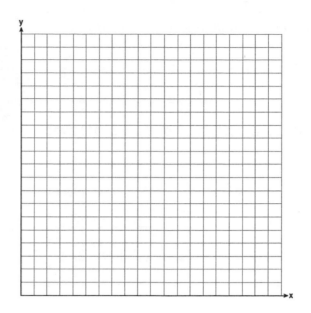

Explain in detail what each coordinate of the point of intersection of these equations means in the context of this problem.

4. What is the solution to the system of equations below?

$$y = 2x + 8$$

$$3(-2x + y) = 12$$

1) no solution

3) $(-1, 6)$

2) infinite solutions

4) $\left(\dfrac{1}{2}, 9\right)$

5.   A system of equations is given below.

08 2016 22

$$x + 2y = 5$$
$$2x + y = 4$$

Which system of equations does *not* have
the same solution?

1) $3x + 6y = 15$ 2) $4x + 8y = 20$
    $2x + y = 4$ $2x + y = 4$

3) $x + 2y = 5$ 4) $x + 2y = 5$
    $6x + 3y = 12$ $4x + 2y = 12$

6.   A drama club is selling tickets to the spring
musical. The auditorium holds 200 people.
Tickets cost $12 at the door and $8.50 if
purchased in advance. The drama club has
a goal of selling at least $1000 worth of
tickets to Saturday's show. Write a system
of inequalities that can be used to model this
scenario. If 50 tickets are sold in advance,
what is the minimum of tickets that must be
sold at the door so that the club meets its goal?
Justify your answer.

08 2016 35

08 2016 37

7. For a class picnic, two teachers went to the same store to purchase drinks. One teacher purchased 18 juice boxes and 32 bottles of water, and spent $19.92. The other teacher purchased 14 juice boxes and 26 bottles of water, and spent $15.76.

Write a system of equations to represent the costs of a juice box, j, and a bottle of water, w. Kara said that the juice boxes might have cost 52 cents each and that the bottles of water might have cost 33 cents each.

Use your system of equations to justify that Kara's prices are *not* possible.

Solve your system of equations to determine the actual cost, in dollars, of each juice box

06 2016 05

8. The Celluloid Cinema sold 150 tickets to a movie. Some of these were child tickets and the rest were adult tickets. A child ticket cost $7.75 and an adult ticket cost $10.25. If the cinema sold $1470 worth of tickets, which system of equations could be used to determine how many adult tickets, a, and how many child tickets, c, were sold?

1) $a + c = 150$
$10.25a + 7.75c = 1470$

2) $a + c = 1470$
$10.25a + 7.75c = 150$

3) $a + c = 150$
$7.75a + 10.25c = 1470$

4) $a + c = 1470$
$7.75a + 10.25c = 150$

9.   The line represented by the equation
      $4y + 2x = 33.6$ shares a solution point with
      the line represented by the table below.

06 2016 18

x	y
−5	3.2
−2	3.8
2	4.6
4	5
11	6.4

The solution for this system is

1) $(-14.0, -1.4)$
2) $(-6.8, 5.0)$
3) $(1.9, 4.6)$
4) $(6.0, 5.4)$

10.   The graphs of the functions $f(x) = |x - 3| + 1$
      and $g(x) = 2x + 1$ are drawn.
      Which statement about these
      functions is true?

06 2016 22

1) The solution to $f(x) = g(x)$ is 3.
2) The solution to $f(x) = g(x)$ is 1.
3) The graphs intersect when $y = 1$.
4) The graphs intersect when $x = 3$.

11. The sum of two numbers, *x* and *y*, is more than 8. When you double *x* and add it to *y*, the sum is less than 14.

06 2016 34

Graph the inequalities that represent this scenario on the set of axes below.

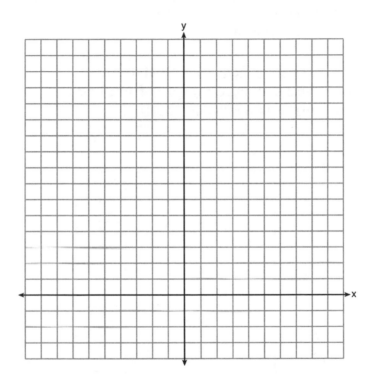

Kai says that the point $(6, 2)$ is a solution to this system. Determine if he is correct and explain your reasoning.

12.   Franco and Caryl went to a bakery to buy
desserts. Franco bought 3 packages of
cupcakes and 2 packages of brownies for
$19. Caryl bought 2 packages of cupcakes
and 4 packages of brownies for $24.
Let *x* equal the price of one package of
cupcakes and *y* equal the price of one
package of brownies.

06 2016 37

Write a system of equations that describes
the given situation. On the set of axes below,
graph the system of equations.

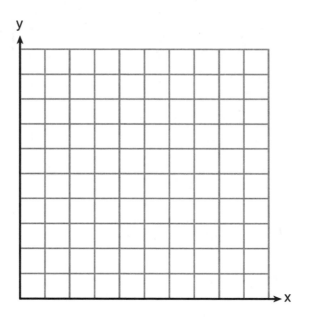

Determine the exact cost of one package of cupcakes and the
exact cost of one package of brownies in dollars and cents.
Justify your solution.

13.   Last week, a candle store received
       $355.60 for selling 20 candles.
       Small candles sell for $10.98 and large
       candles sell for $27.98. How many large
       candles did the store sell?

08 2015 10

       1) 6
       2) 8
       3) 10
       4) 12

14.   Mo's farm stand sold a total of 165 pounds
       of apples and peaches. She sold apples for
       $1.75 per pound and peaches for $2.50
       per pound. If she made $337.50, how many
       pounds of peaches did she sell?

06 2015 06

       1) 11
       2) 18
       3) 65
       4) 100

15. Albert says that the two systems of equations shown below have the same solutions.

06 2015 33

First System	Second System
$8x + 9y = 48$	$8x + 9y = 48$
$12x + 5y = 21$	$-8.5y = -51$

Determine and state whether you agree with Albert. Justify your answer.

16. Two functions, $y = |x - 3|$ and $3x + 3y = 27$, are graphed on the same set of axes. Which statement is true about the solution to the system of equations?

01 2015 18

1) $(3,0)$ is the solution to the system because it satisfies the equation $y = |x - 3|$.

2) $(9,0)$ is the solution to the system because it satisfies the equation $3x + 3y = 27$.

3) $(6,3)$ is the solution to the system because it satisfies both equations.

4) $(3,0)$, $(9,0)$, and $(6,3)$ are the solutions to the system of equations because they all satisfy at least one of the equations.

17. Jacob and Zachary go to the movie theater and purchase refreshments for their friends. Jacob spends a total of $18.25 on two bags of popcorn and three drinks. Zachary spends a total of $27.50 for four bags of popcorn and two drinks. Write a system of equations that can be used to find the price of one bag of popcorn and the price of one drink. Using these equations, determine and state the price of a bag of popcorn and the price of a drink, to the *nearest cent*.

01 2015 33

QUADRATIC EQUATIONS AND FACTORING

1. An Air Force pilot is flying at a cruising altitude of 9000 feet and is forced to eject from her aircraft. The function $h(t) = -16t^2 + 128t + 9000$ models the height, in feet, of the pilot above the ground, where *t* is the time, in seconds, after she is ejected from the aircraft.

   08 2017 36

   Determine and state the vertex of $h(t)$. $h(4) = 4,$ 9256

   Explain what the second coordinate of the vertex represents in the context of the problem.

   After the pilot was ejected, what is the maximum number of feet she was above the aircraft's cruising altitude? 256 ft.

   Justify your answer.

2. Solve the equation $x^2 - 6x = 15$ by completing the square.

   08 2017 32

   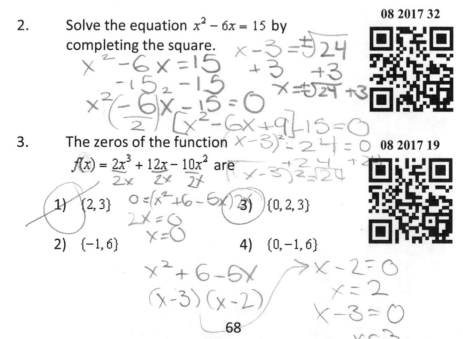

3. The zeros of the function
   $f(x) = 2x^3 + 12x - 10x^2$ are

   08 2017 19

   1) $\{2, 3\}$ 3) $\{0, 2, 3\}$

   2) $\{-1, 6\}$ 4) $\{0, -1, 6\}$

4.   The expression $49x^2 - 36$ is equivalent to   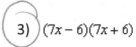 **08 2017 03**

   1) $(7x - 6)^2$ 3) $(7x - 6)(7x + 6)$

   2) $(24.5x - 18)^2$ 4) $(24.5x - 18)(24.5x + 18)$

5.   What are the solutions to the equation   **06 2017 22**
   $x^2 - 8x = 10$?

   1) $4 \pm \sqrt{10}$ 3) $-4 \pm \sqrt{10}$

   2) $4 \pm \sqrt{26}$ 4) $-4 \pm \sqrt{26}$

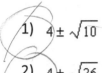

$$x^2 \left(\frac{-8}{2}\right)^2 x - 10 = 0$$

6.   Which expression is equivalent to $16x^4 - 64$?   **06 2017 06**

   1) $(4x^2 - 8)^2$ 3) $(4x^2 + 8)(4x^2 - 8)$

   2) $(8x^2 - 32)^2$ 4) $(8x^2 + 32)(8x^2 - 32)$

7.   Which expression is equivalent to $36x^2 - 100$?   **08 2016 08**

   1) $4(3x - 5)(3x - 5)$
   2) $4(3x + 5)(3x - 5)$
   3) $2(9x - 25)(9x - 25)$
   4) $2(9x + 25)(9x - 25)$

8. The height of a rocket, at selected times, is shown in the table below.

08 2016 13

Time (sec)	0	1	2	3	4	5	6	7
Height (ft)	180	260	308	324	308	260	180	68

Based on these data, which statement is *not* a valid conclusion?

1) The rocket was launched from a height of 180 feet.
2) The maximum height of the rocket occurred 3 seconds after launch.
3) The rocket was in the air approximately 6 seconds before hitting the ground.
4) The rocket was above 300 feet for approximately 2 seconds.

9. What are the solutions to the equation $3x^2 + 10x = 8$?

08 2016 19

1) $\frac{2}{3}$ and -4

2) $-\frac{2}{3}$ and 4

3) $\frac{4}{3}$ and -2

4) $-\frac{4}{3}$ and 2

10. The function $f(x) = 3x^2 + 12x + 11$ can be written in vertex form as

08 2016 21

1) $f(x) = (3x + 6)^2 - 25$
2) $f(x) = 3(x + 6)^2 - 25$
3) $f(x) = 3(x + 2)^2 - 1$
4) $f(x) = 3(x + 2)^2 + 7$

08 2016 31

11. Find the zeros of $f(x) = (x - 3)^2 - 49$, algebraically.

$X = -4$
$X = 10$

12. Janice is asked to solve $0 = 64x^2 + 16x - 3$. She begins the problem by writing the following steps:

08 2016 36

Line 1 $0 = 64x^2 + 16x - 3$
Line 2 $0 = B^2 + 2B - 3$
Line 3 $0 = (B + 3)(B - 1)$

Use Janice's procedure to solve the equation for x. $X = -3/8$ $X = 1/8$

Explain the method Janice used to solve the quadratic equation.

71

13. Which equation and ordered pair represent the correct vertex form and vertex for $j(x) = x^2 - 12x + 7$?

06 2016 16

    1) $j(x) = (x - 6)^2 + 43,\ (6, 43)$
    2) $j(x) = (x - 6)^2 + 43,\ (-6, 43)$
    3) $j(x) = (x - 6)^2 - 29,\ (6, -29)$
    4) $j(x) = (x - 6)^2 - 29,\ (-6, -29)$

14. What is the solution of the equation $2(x + 2)^2 - 4 = 28$?

06 2016 19

    1) 6, only
    2) 2, only
    3) 2 and −6
    4) 6 and −2

15. Amy solved the equation $2x^2 + 5x - 42 = 0$. She stated that the solutions to the equation were $\dfrac{7}{2}$ and −6.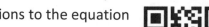

06 2016 28

Do you agree with Amy's solutions? Explain why or why not.

16. The height, *H*, in feet, of an object dropped from the top of a building after *t* seconds is given by $H(t) = -16t^2 + 144$. How many feet did the object fall between one and two seconds after it was dropped? Determine, algebraically, how many seconds it will take for the object to reach the ground.

06 2016 33

17. The zeros of the function
$f(x) = 3x^2 - 3x - 6$ are

08 2015 13

1) -1 and -2
2) 1 and -2
3) 1 and 2
4) -1 and 2

18. If $f(x) = x^2 - 2x - 8$ and $g(x) = \frac{1}{4}x - 1$,
for which value of x is $f(x) = g(x)$?

08 2015 17

1) -1.75 and -1.438
2) -1.75 and 4
3) -1.438 and 0
4) 4 and 0

19. If Lylah completes the square for
$f(x) = x^2 - 12x + 7$ in order to find the
minimum, she must write $f(x)$ in the
general form $f(x) = (x - a)^2 + b$.
What is the value of a for $f(x)$?

08 2015 20

1)   6   2) -6

3)   12   4) -12

20. The solution of the equation
$(x + 3)^2 = 7$ is

08 2015 23

1) $3 \pm \sqrt{7}$ 2) $7 \pm \sqrt{3}$

3) $-3 \pm \sqrt{7}$ 4) $-7 \pm \sqrt{3}$

21. How many real solutions does the equation $x^2 - 2x + 5 = 0$ have? Justify your answer.

08 2015 29

No real solutions.

22. A toy rocket is launched from the ground straight upward. The height of the rocket above the ground, in feet, is given by the equation $h(t) = -16t^2 + 64t$, where t is the time in seconds. Determine the domain for this function in the given context. Explain your reasoning.

08 2015 31

$$t = -16t^2 + 64$$

23. A rectangular picture measures 6 inches by 8 inches. Simon wants to build a wooden frame for the picture so that the framed picture takes up a maximum area of 100 square inches on his wall. The pieces of wood that he uses to build the frame all have the same width. Write an equation or inequality that could be used to determine the maximum width of the pieces of wood for the frame Simon could create. Explain how your equation or inequality models the situation. Solve the equation or inequality to determine the maximum width of the pieces of wood used for the frame to the *nearest tenth of an inch*.

08 2015 37

24. If the area of a rectangle is expressed as $x^4 - 9y^2$, then the product of the length and the width of t he rectangle could be expressed as

06 2015 03

1) $(x - 3y)(x + 3y)$
2) $(x^2 - 3y)(x^2 + 3y)$
3) $(x^2 - 3y)(x^2 - 3y)$
4) $(x^4 + y)(x - 9y)$

25. What are the zeros of the function $f(x) = x^2 - 13x - 30$?

06 2015 10

1) −10 and 3
2) 10 and −3
3) −15 and 2
4) 15 and −2

26. Which quadratic function has the largest maximum?

06 2015 14

x	f(x)
−1	−3
0	5
1	9
2	9
3	5
4	−3

1) $h(x) = (3 - x)(2 + x)$ **2)**

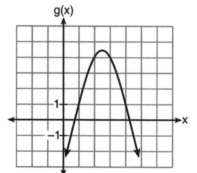

3) $k(x) = -5x^2 - 12x + 4$ **4)**

27. When directed to solve a quadratic equation by completing the square, Sam arrived at the equation

06 2015 18

$\left(x - \dfrac{5}{2}\right)^2 = \dfrac{13}{4}$. Which equation could have been the original equation given to Sam?

1) $x^2 + 5x + 7 = 0$ 2) $x^2 + 5x + 3 = 0$

3) $x^2 - 5x + 7 = 0$ 4) $x^2 - 5x + 3 = 0$

28. What are the solutions to the equation $x^2 - 8x = 24$?

06 2015 23

1) $x = 4 \pm 2\sqrt{10}$ 2) $x = -4 \pm 2\sqrt{10}$

3) $x = 4 \pm 2\sqrt{2}$ 4) $x = -4 \pm 2\sqrt{2}$

29. John and Sarah are each saving money for a car. The total amount of money John will save is given by the function $f(x) = 60 + 5x$. The total amount of money Sarah will save is given by the function $g(x) = x^2 + 46$. After how many weeks, x, will they have the same amount of money saved? Explain how you arrived at your answer.

06 2015 27

30. A landscaper is creating a rectangular flower bed such that the width is half of the length. The area of the flower bed is 34 square feet. Write and solve an equation to determine the width of the flower bed, to the *nearest tenth of a foot*

06 2015 32

31. A football player attempts to kick a football over a goal post. The path of the football can be modeled by the function

06 2015 37

$h(x) = -\dfrac{1}{225}x^2 + \dfrac{2}{3}x$, where x is the horizontal distance from the kick, and $h(x)$ is the height of the football above the ground, when both are measured in feet. On the set of axes below, graph the function $y = h(x)$ over the interval $0 \le x \le 150$.

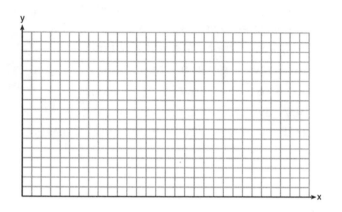

Determine the vertex of $y = h(x)$. Interpret the meaning of this vertex in the context of the problem. The goal post is 10 feet high and 45 yards away from the kick. Will the ball be high enough to pass over the goal post? Justify your answer.

32. Which equation has the same solutions as $2x^2 + x - 3 = 0$

01 2015 03

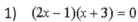

1) $(2x - 1)(x + 3) = 0$
2) $(2x + 1)(x - 3) = 0$
3) $(2x - 3)(x + 1) = 0$
4) $(2x + 3)(x - 1) = 0$

33. Which equation has the same solutions as $x^2 + 6x - 7 = 0$

01 2015 17

1) $(x + 3)^2 = 2$
2) $(x - 3)^2 = 2$
3) $(x - 3)^2 = 16$
4) $(x + 3)^2 = 16$

34. When factored completely, the expression $p^4 - 81$ is equivalent to

01 2015 22

1) $(p^2 + 9)(p^2 - 9)$
2) $(p^2 - 9)(p^2 - 9)$
3) $(p^2 + 9)(p + 3)(p - 3)$
4) $(p + 3)(p - 3)(p + 3)(p - 3)$

35. A polynomial function contains the factors x, $x - 2$, and $x + 5$. Which graph(s) below could represent the graph of this function?

01 2015 24

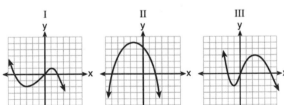

1) I, only
2) II, only
3) I and III

79

36.   Solve the equation $4x^2 - 12x = 7$
       algebraically for *x*.

01 2015 29

37.   Given the function $f(x) = -x^2 + 8x + 9$.
       Rewrite *f(x)* in vertex form by
       completing the square.

01 2015 36b

REGRESSIONS

1. The results of a linear regression are shown below.

    08 2017 22

    $$y = ax + b$$

    $$a = -1.15785$$

    $$b = 139.3171772$$

    $$r = -0.896557832$$

    $$r^2 = 0.8038159461$$

    Which phrase best describes the relationship between x and y?

    1) strong negative correlation

    3) weak negative correlation

    2) strong positive correlation

    4) weak positive correlation

2. Bella recorded data and used her graphing calculator to find the equation for the line of best fit. She then used the correlation coefficient to determine the strength of the linear fit. Which correlation coefficient represents the strongest linear relationship?

    06 2017 14

    1) 0.9

    3) −0.3

    2) 0.5

    4) −0.8

3.   The table below shows 6 students' overall averages and their averages in their math class.

08 2016 06

Overall Student Average	92	98	84	80	75	82
Math Class Average	91	95	85	85	75	78

If a linear model is applied to these data, which statement best describes the correlation coefficient?

1) It is close to −1.
2) It is close to 1.
3) It is close to 0.
4) It is close to 0.5.

4.   The data table below shows the
median diameter of grains of
sand and the slope of the beach
for 9 naturally occurring ocean beaches.

08 2016 33

Median Diameter of Grains of Sand, in Millimeters (x)	0.17	0.19	0.22	0.235	0.235	0.3	0.35	0.42	0.85
Slope of Beach, in Degrees (y)	0.63	0.7	0.82	0.88	1.15	1.5	4.4	7.3	11.3

Write the linear regression equation for this
set of data, rounding all values to the *nearest
thousandth*.

Using this equation, predict the slope of a beach,
to the *nearest tenth of a degree*, on a beach with
grains of sand having a median diameter of 0.65 mm.

5.   The scatterplot below compares the
     Number of bags of popcorn and the
     number of sodas sold at each
     performance of the circus over
     one week.

06 2016 04

Popcorn Sales and Soda Sales

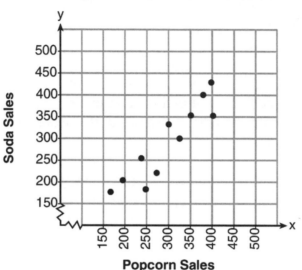

Which conclusion can be drawn from the scatterplot?

1) There is a negative correlation between popcorn
   sales and soda sales.
2) There is a positive correlation between popcorn
   sales and soda sales.
3) There is no correlation between popcorn sales
   and soda sales.
4) Buying popcorn causes people to buy soda.

6.   The table below shows the attendance at a museum in select years from 2007 to 2013.

08 2015 36

Attendance at Museum

Year	2007	2008	2009	2011	2013
Attendance (millions)	8.3	8.5	8.5	8.8	9.3

State the linear regression equation represented by the data table when $x = 0$ is used to represent the year 2007 and y is used to represent the attendance. Round all values to the *nearest hundredth*.

State the correlation coefficient to the *nearest hundredth* and determine whether the data suggest a strong or weak association.

7. Beverly did a study this past spring using data she collected from a cafeteria. She recorded data weekly for ice cream sales and soda sales. Beverly found the line of best fit and the correlation coefficient, as shown in the diagram below.

06 2015 16

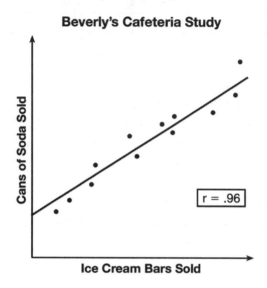

Beverly's Cafeteria Study

Cans of Soda Sold

$r = .96$

Ice Cream Bars Sold

Given this information, which statement(s) can correctly be concluded?

I. Eating more ice cream causes a person to become thirsty.

II. Drinking more soda causes a person to become hungry.

III. There is a strong correlation between ice cream sales and soda sales.

1) I, only 2) III, only

3) I and III 4) II and III

8.   The residual plots from two different sets
of bivariate data are graphed below.

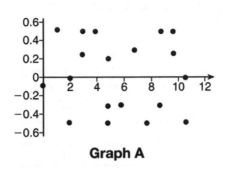

Graph A

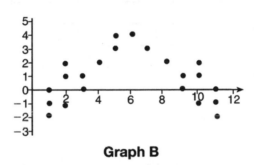

Graph B

Explain, using evidence from graph *A* and graph *B*, which
graph indicates that the model for the data is a good fit.

9. A nutritionist collected information about different brands of beef hot dogs. She made a table showing the number of Calories and the amount of sodium in each hot dog.

01 2015 35

Calories per Beef Hot Dog	Milligrams of Sodium per Beef Hot Dog
186	495
181	477
176	425
149	322
184	482
190	587
158	370
139	322

a) Write the correlation coefficient for the line of best fit.

Round your answer to the *nearest hundredth.*

b) Explain what the correlation coefficient suggests in the context of this problem.

EXPONENTIAL EQUATIONS

1.   The Ebola virus has an infection rate of
      11% per day as compared to the SARS
      virus, which has a rate of 4% per day. If
      there were one case of Ebola and 30 cases
      of SARS initially reported to authorities and
      cases are reported each day, which
      statement is true?

08 2017 21

    1) At day 10 and day 53   3) At day 10 there are
       there are more Ebola   more SARS cases, but at
       cases.   day 53 there are more
              Ebola cases.

    2) At day 10 and day 53   4) At day 10 there are
       there are more SARS   more Ebola cases, but at
       cases.   day 53 there are more
              SARS cases.

2.   Mario's $15,000 car depreciates in value at
      a rate of 19% per year. The value, *V*, after *t*
      years can be modeled by the function
      $V = 15,000(0.81)^t$.

08 2017 16

Which function is equivalent
to the original function?

    1) $V = 15,000(0.9)^{9t}$ 3) $V = 15,000(0.9)^{\frac{t}{9}}$

    2) $V = 15,000(0.9)^{2t}$ 4) $V = 15,000(0.9)^{\frac{t}{2}}$

3. If a population of 100 cells triples every hour, which function represents $p(t)$, the population after *t* hours?

08 2017 14

1) $p(t) = 3(100)^t$

3) $p(t) = 3t + 100$

2) $p(t) = 100(3)^t$

4) $p(t) = 100t + 3$

4. Michael has $10 in his savings account. Option 1 will add $100 to his account each week. Option 2 will double the amount in his account at the end of each week. Write a function in terms of *x* to model each option of saving. Michael wants to have at least $700 in his account at the end of 7 weeks to buy a mountain bike.

06 2017 36

Determine which option(s) will enable him to reach his goal. Justify your answer.

5. Anne invested $1000 in an account with a
    1.3% annual interest rate. She made no
    deposits or withdrawals on the account for
    2 years. If interest was compounded annually,
    which equation represents the balance in the
    account after the 2 years?

    06 2017 12

    1) $A = 1000(1 - 0.013)^2$ 3) $A = 1000(1 - 1.3)^2$

    2) $A = 1000(1 + 0.013)^2$ 4) $A = 1000(1 + 1.3)^2$

6. Vinny collects population data, $P(h)$,
    about a specific strain of bacteria over
    time in hours, h, as shown in the graph
    below.

    06 2017 07

    P(h)

    (3,32)

    (2,16)

    (1,8)

    (0,4)

    h

    Which equation represents the graph of $P(h)$?

    1) $P(h) = 4(2)^h$ 3) $P(h) = 3h^2 + 0.2h + 4.2$

    2) $P(h) = \dfrac{46}{5}h + \dfrac{6}{5}$ 4) $P(h) = \dfrac{2}{3}h^3 - h^2 + 3h + 4$

7. The table below shows the temperature, $T(m)$, of a cup of hot chocolate that is allowed to chill over several minutes, m.

08 2016 17

Time, m (minutes)	0	2	4	6	8
Temperature, T(m) (°F)	150	108	78	56	41

Which expression best fits the data for $T(m)$?

1) $150(0.85)^m$

2) $150(1.15)^m$

3) $150(0.85)^{m-1}$

4) $150(1.15)^{m-1}$

8. Milton has his money invested in a stock portfolio. The value, $v(x)$, of his portfolio can be modeled with the function $v(x) = 30,000(0.78)^x$, where x is the number of years since he made his investment. Which statement describes the rate of change of the value of his portfolio?

08 2016 24

1) It decreases 78% per year.
2) It decreases 22% per year.
3) It increases 78% per year.
4) It increases 22% per year.

9. Consider the pattern of squares shown below: 08 2016 27

Which type of model, linear or exponential, should be used to determine how many squares are in the *n*th pattern?
Explain your answer.

10. The growth of a certain organism can be modeled by $C(t) = 10(1.029)^{24t}$, where $C(t)$ is the total number of cells after *t* hours. Which function is approximately equivalent to $C(t)$?   06 2016 14

1) $C(t) = 240(.083)^{24t}$

2) $C(t) = 10(.083)^{t}$

3) $C(t) = 10(1.986)^{t}$

4) $C(t) = 240(1.986)^{\frac{t}{24}}$

11. A student invests $500 for 3 years in a savings account that earns 4% interest per year. No further deposits or withdrawals are made during this time. Which statement does not yield the correct balance in the account at the end of 3 years?   06 2016 17

1) $500(1.04)^{3}$
2) $500(1-.04)^{3}$
3) $500(1+.04)(1+.04)(1+.04)$
4) $500 + 500(.04) + 520(.04) + 540.8(.04)$

12. The country of Benin in West Africa has a population of 9.05 million people. The population is growing at a rate of 3.1% each year. Which function can be used to find the population 7 years from now?

08 2015 07

1) $f(t) = (9.05 \times 10^6)(1 - 0.31)^7$
2) $f(t) = (9.05 \times 10^6)(1 + 0.31)^7$
3) $f(t) = (9.05 \times 10^6)(1 + 0.031)^7$
4) $f(t) = (9.05 \times 10^6)(1 - 0.031)^7$

13. Rachel and Marc were given the information shown below about the bacteria growing in a Petri dish in their biology class.

08 2015 27

Number of Hours, x	1	2	3	4	5	6	7	8	9	10
Number of Bacteria, B(x)	220	280	350	440	550	690	860	1070	1340	1680

Rachel wants to model this information with a linear function. Marc wants to use an exponential function. Which model is the better choice? Explain why you chose this model.

14. The number of carbon atoms in a
fossil is given by the function
$y = 5100(0.95)^x$, where x represents
the number of years since being
discovered. What is the percent
of change each year? Explain how you
arrived at your answer.

08 2015 30

15. Graph $f(x) = x^2$ and $g(x) = 2^x$ for
$x \geq 0$ on the set of axes below.

08 2015 33

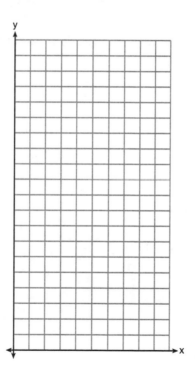

State which function, $f(x)$ or $g(x)$, has a
greater value when $x = 20$. Justify your reasoning.

16. A laboratory technician studied the population growth of a colony of bacteria. He recorded the number of bacteria every other day, as shown in the partial table below.

06 2015 13

t (time, in days)	0	2	4
f(t) (bacteria)	25	15,625	9,765,625

Which function would accurately model the technician's data?

1) $f(t) = 25^t$

2) $f(t) = 25^{t+1}$

3) $f(t) = 25t$

4) $f(t) = 25(t+1)$

17. An application developer released a new app to be downloaded. The table below gives the number of downloads for the first four weeks after the launch of the app.

06 2015 36

Number of Weeks	1	2	3	4
Number of Downloads	120	180	270	405

Write an exponential equation that models these data. Use this model to predict how many downloads the developer would expect in the 26th week if this trend continues. Round your answer to the nearest download. Would it be reasonable to use this model to predict the number of downloads past one year? Explain your reasoning.

18. Krystal was given $3000 when she turned 2 years old. Her parents invested it at a 2% interest rate compounded annually. No deposits or withdrawals were made. Which expression can be used to determine how much money Krystal had in the account when she turned 18?

01 2015 04

1) $3000(1 + 0.02)^{16}$
2) $3000(1 - 0.02)^{16}$
3) $3000(1 + 0.02)^{18}$
4) $3000(1 - 0.02)^{18}$

19. The value in dollars, $v(x)$, of a certain car after x years is represented by the equation $v(x) = 25,000(0.86)^x$. To the *nearest dollar*, how much more is the car worth after 2 years than after 3 years?

01 2015 08

    1) 2589
    2) 6510
    3) 15,901
    4) 18,490

20. Some banks charge a fee on savings accounts that are left inactive for an extended period of time. The equation $y = 5000(0.98)^x$ represents the value, y, of one account that was left inactive for a period of x years. What is the y-intercept of this equation and what does it represent?

01 2015 15

    1) 0.98, the percent of money in the account initially
    2) 0.98, the percent of money in the account after x years
    3) 5000, the amount of money in the account initially
    4) 5000, the amount of money in the account after x years

21. Miriam and Jessica are growing bacteria in a laboratory. Miriam uses the growth function $f(t) = n^{2t}$ while Jessica uses the function $g(t) = n^{4t}$, where n represents the initial number of bacteria and t is the time, in hours. If Miriam starts with 16 bacteria, how many bacteria should Jessica start with to achieve the same growth over time?

01 2015 19

1) 32   2) 16

3) 8   4) 4

22. Write an exponential equation for the graph shown below.

01 2015 32

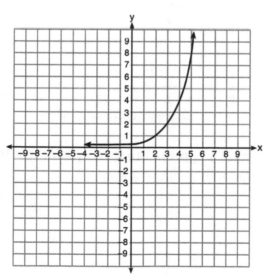

Explain how you determined the equation.

GRAPHING

1. Samantha purchases a package of sugar cookies. The nutrition label states that each serving size of 3 cookies contains 160 Calories. Samantha creates the graph below showing the number of cookies eaten and the number of Calories consumed.

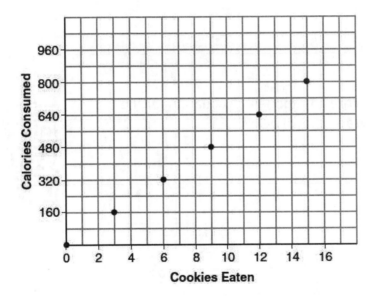

Explain why it is appropriate for Samantha to draw a line through the points on the graph.

2.   How many of the equations listed below   **08 2017 20**
represent the line passing through the
points $(2, 3)$ and $(4, -7)$?

$$5x + y = 13$$

$$y + 7 = -5(x - 4)$$

$$y = -5x + 13$$

$$y - 7 = 5(x - 4)$$

1)   1   3)   3

2)   2   4)   4

3.   The function $h(x)$, which is graphed below,   **08 2017 18**
and the function $g(x) = 2|x + 4| - 3$ are given.

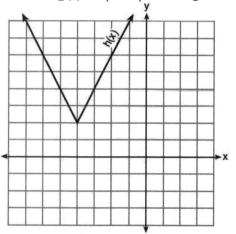

Which statements about these functions are true?

I. $g(x)$ has a lower minimum value than $h(x)$.

II.   For all values of x, $h(x) < g(x)$.

III.   For any value of x, $g(x) \neq h(x)$.

1) I and II, only   3)

2) I and III, only   4) I, II, and III

4.   In the functions $f(x) = kx^2$ and $g(x) = |kx|$,   08 2017 06
        k is a positive integer. If k is replaced

        by $\frac{1}{2}$, which statement about these

        new functions is true?

1)   The graphs of both $f(x)$ and $g(x)$ become wider.
2)   The graph of $f(x)$ becomes narrower and the
        graph of $g(x)$ shifts left.
3)   The graphs of both $f(x)$ and $g(x)$ shift vertically.
4)   The graph of $f(x)$ shifts left and the graph of
        $g(x)$ becomes wider.

5. The graph below models Craig's trip to visit his friend in another state. In the course of his travels, he encountered both highway and city driving.

06 2017 34

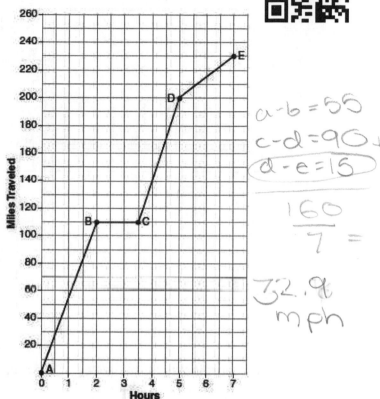

$a - b = 55$

$c - d = 90 +$

$d - e = 15$

$\dfrac{160}{7} =$

32.9 mph

Based on the graph, during which interval did Craig most likely drive in the city? Explain your reasoning. Explain what might have happened in the interval between *B* and *C*. Determine Craig's average speed, to the *nearest tenth of a mile per hour*, for his entire trip.

interval $d \to e$. Slowest, most traffic. $B \to C =$ rest. 22.9 mph.

6.   Graph the function $f(x) = -x^2 - 6x$ on the set of axes below.

06 2017 26

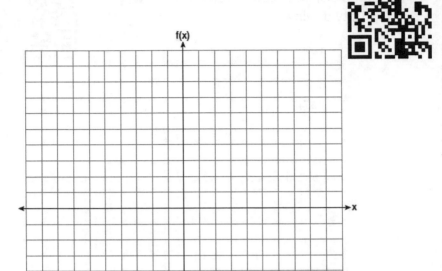

State the coordinates of the vertex of the graph.

7. The graph of a quadratic function is shown below.

06 2017 16

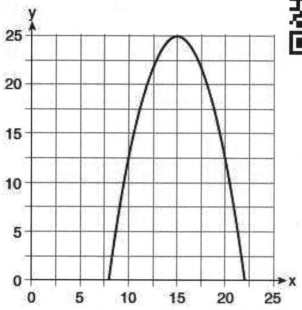

An equation that represents the function could be

1) $q(x) = \dfrac{1}{2}(x + 15)^2 - 25$

3) $q(x) = \dfrac{1}{2}(x - 15)^2 + 25$

2) $q(x) = -\dfrac{1}{2}(x + 15)^2 - 25$

4) $q(x) = -\dfrac{1}{2}(x - 15)^2 + 25$

8.   Which graph represents $y = \sqrt{x-2}$?

1)

3)

2)

4)

9.   To keep track of his profits, the owner of a carnival booth decided to model his ticket sales on a graph. He found that his profits only declined when he sold between 10 and 40 tickets. Which graph could represent his profits?

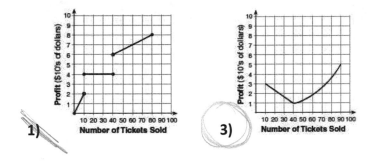

1)

3)

106

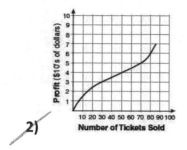

2)

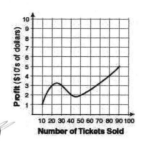

4)

10. The solution of an equation with two variables, x and y, is

08 2016 02

1) the set of all x values that make $y = 0$
2) the set of all y values that make $x = 0$
3) the set of all ordered pairs, (x,y), that make the equation true
4) the set of all ordered pairs, (x,y), where the graph of the equation crosses the y-axis

11. Which function has the greatest y-intercept?

08 2016 11

1) $f(x) = 3x$
2) $2x + 3y = 12$
3) the line that has a slope of 2 and passes through $(1,-4)$
4)

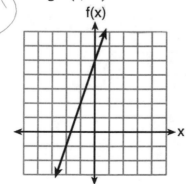

12. Based on the graph below, which expression is a possible factorization of $p(x)$?

08 2016 23

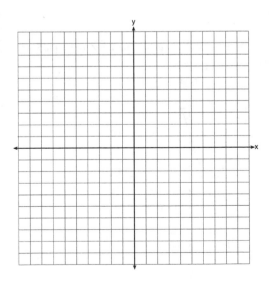

1) $(x+3)(x-2)(x-4)$
2) $(x-3)(x+2)(x+4)$
3) $(x+3)(x-5)(x-2)(x-4)$
4) $(x-3)(x+5)(x+2)(x+4)$

13. Graph the function $y = -\sqrt{x+3}$ on the set of axes below.

08 2016 25

14.   On the set of axes   below,
      draw the graph of $y = x^2 - 4x - 1$.

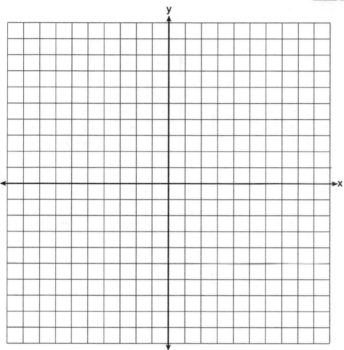

State the equation of the axis of symmetry.

15.   On the set of axes below, graph

$$g(x) = \frac{1}{2}x + 1$$

and

$$f(x) = \begin{cases} 2x + 1, & x \le -1 \\ 2 - x^2, & x > -1 \end{cases}$$

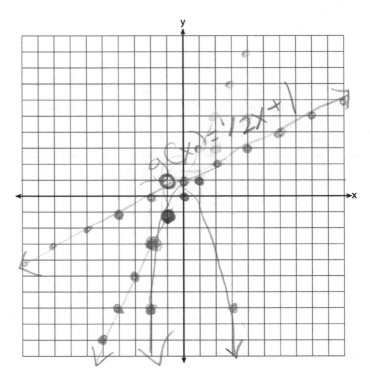

How many values of x satisfy the equation $f(x) = g(x)$? Explain your answer, using evidence from your graphs.

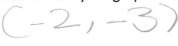

16. Given the graph of the line represented by the equation $f(x) = -2x + b$, if b is increased by 4 units, the graph of the new line would be shifted 4 units

08 2015 01

1) right
2) up
3) left
4) down

17. Which graph represents $f(x) = \begin{cases} |x| & x < 1 \\ \sqrt{x} & x \geq 1 \end{cases}$?

08 2015 16

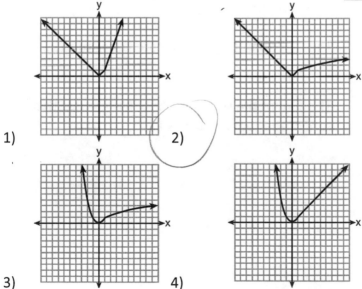

1) 2) 3) 4)

18. Given the following quadratic functions: 08 2015 21

$$g(x) = -x^2 - x + 6$$

and

x	-3	-2	-1	0	1	2	3	4	5
n(x)	-7	0	5	8	9	8	5	0	-7

Which statement about these functions is true?

1) Over the interval $-1 \le x \le 1$, the average rate of change for $n(x)$ is less than that for $g(x)$.

2) The y-intercept of $g(x)$ is greater than the y-intercept for $n(x)$.

3) The function $g(x)$ has a greater maximum value than $n(x)$.

4) The sum of the roots of $n(x) = 0$ is greater than the sum of the roots of $g(x) = 0$.

19.   A driver leaves home for a business trip   08 2015 28
and drives at a constant speed of 60
miles per hour for 2 hours. Her car gets a
flat tire, and she spends 30 minutes
changing the tire. She resumes driving and
drives at 30 miles per hour for the
remaining one hour until she reaches her
destination.

On the set of axes below, draw a graph that
models the driver's distance from home.

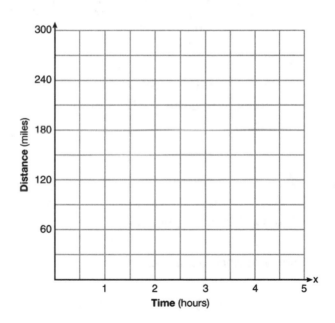

20. The graph below represents a jogger's speed during her 20-minute jog around her neighborhood.

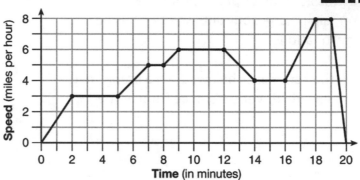

Which statement best describes what the jogger was doing during the 9 – 12 minute interval of her jog?

1) She was standing still.

2) She was increasing her speed.

3) She was decreasing her speed

4) She was jogging at a constant rate.

21.   Morgan can start wrestling at age 5 in
        Division 1. He remains in that division
        until his next odd birthday when he is
        required to move up to the next division
        level. Which graph correctly represents
        this information?

06 2015 07

1)

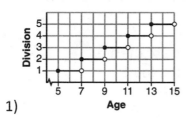

2)

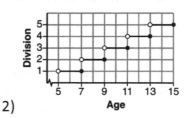

3)

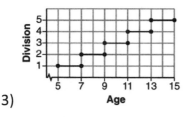

4)

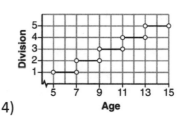

22.   Joey enlarged a 3-inch by 5-inch photograph on a copy machine. He enlarged it four times. The table below shows the area of the photograph after each enlargement.

06 2015 11

Enlargement	0	1	2	3	4
Area (square inches)	15	18.8	23.4	29.3	36.6

What is the average rate of change of the area from the original photograph to the fourth enlargement, to the *nearest tenth*?

1)   4.3   2) 4.5

3)   5.4   4) 6.0

23. Which equation(s) represent the graph below?

06 2015 12

I $y = (x + 2)(x^2 - 4x - 12)$

II $y = (x - 3)(x^2 + x - 2)$

III $y = (x - 1)(x^2 - 5x - 6)$

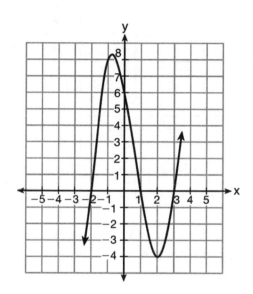

1)   I, only   2)   II, only

3)   I and II   4)   II and III

24. Graph the function $y = |x - 3|$ on the set of axes below.

06 2015 25

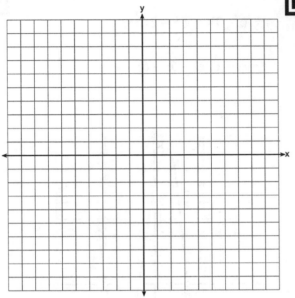

Explain how the graph of $y = |x - 3|$ has changed from the related graph $y = |x|$.

25.   Which table of values represents
       a linear relationship?

01 2015 05

1)

x	f(x)
−1	−3
0	−2
1	1
2	6
3	13

2)

x	f(x)
−1	$\frac{1}{2}$
0	1
1	2
2	4
3	8

3)

x	f(x)
−1	−3
0	−1
1	1
2	3
3	5

4)

x	f(x)
−1	−1
0	0
1	1
2	8
3	27

26. Which function has the same *y*-intercept as the graph below?

01 2015 09

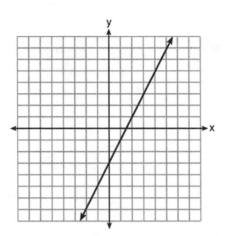

1) $y = \dfrac{12 - 6x}{4}$ 2) $27 + 3y = 6x$

3) $6y + x = 18$ 4) $y + 3 = 6x$

27. The graph of a linear equation contains the points $(3,11)$ and $(-2,1)$. Which point also lies on the graph?

01 2015 11

1) $(2,1)$ 2) $(2,4)$

3) $(2,6)$ 4) $(2,9)$

28. How does the graph of $f(x) = 3(x-2)^2 + 1$ compare to the graph of $g(x) = x^2$?

01 2015 12

1) The graph of $f(x)$ is wider than the graph of $g(x)$, and its vertex is moved to the left 2 units and up 1 unit.
2) The graph of $f(x)$ is narrower than the graph of $g(x)$, and its vertex is moved to the right 2 units and up 1 unit.
3) The graph of $f(x)$ is narrower than the graph of $g(x)$, and its vertex is moved to the left 2 units and up 1 unit.
4) The graph of $f(x)$ is wider than the graph of $g(x)$, and its vertex is moved to the right 2 units and up 1 unit.

29. Given the function $f(x) = -x^2 + 8x + 9$, state whether the vertex represents a maximum or minimum point for the function. Explain your answer.

01 2015 36a

STATISTICS

1.   The heights, in feet, of former New York
       Knicks basketball players are listed
       below.

08 2017 34

6.4, 6.9, 6.3, 6.2, 6.3, 6.0, 6.1, 6.3, 6.8,
6.2, 6.5, 7.1, 6.4, 6.3, 6.5, 6.5, 6.4, 7.0,
6.4, 6.3, 6.2, 6.3, 7.0, 6.4, 6.5, 6.5, 6.5, 6.0, 6.2

Using the heights given, complete the frequency
table below.

Interval	Frequency
6.0-6.1	
6.2-6.3	
6.4-6.5	
6.6-6.7	
6.8-6.9	
7.0-7.1	

Based on the frequency table created, draw and label a
frequency histogram on the grid below.

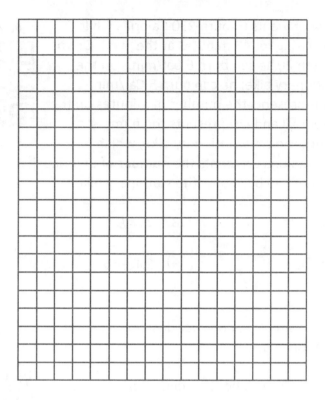

Determine and state which interval contains the
upper quartile. Justify your response.

2. Konnor wants to burn 250 Calories while
    exercising for 45 minutes at the gym. On the
    treadmill, he can burn 6 Cal/min. On the
    stationary bike, he can burn 5 Cal/min.
    If *t* represents the number of minutes on the
    treadmill and *b* represents the number of
    minutes on the stationary bike, which
    expression represents the number of Calories that
    Konnor can burn on   the stationary bike?

    08 2017 12

    1) b 3) $45 - b$

    2) $5b$ 4) $250 - 5b$

3. Which situation does *not* describe a causal
    relationship?

    08 2017 08

    1) The higher the volume on a radio,
        the louder the sound will be.

    2) The faster a student types a research
        paper, the more pages the paper will
        have.

    3) The shorter the distance driven, the
        less gasoline that will be used.

    4) The slower the pace of a runner, the
        longer it will take the runner to finish
        the race.

4. A survey of 100 students was taken. It was found that 60 students watched sports, and 34 of these students did not like pop music. Of the students who did *not* watch sports, 70% liked pop music. Complete the two-way frequency table.

06 2017 29

	Watch Sports	Don't Watch Sports	Total
Like Pop			
Don't Like Pop			
Total			

5. The heights, in inches, of 12 students are listed below.

06 2017 15

61,67,72,62,65,59,60,79,60,61,64,63

Which statement best describes the spread of these data?

1) The set of data is evenly spread.

3) The set of data is skewed because 59 is the only value below 60.

2) The median of the data is 59.5.

4) 79 is an outlier, which would affect the standard deviation of these data.

6.   Which statistic can *not* be determined from   08 2016 03
a box plot representing the scores on a
math test in Mrs. DeRidder's algebra class?

1)   the lowest score
2)   the median score
3)   the highest score
4)   the score that occurs most frequently

7.   A public opinion poll was taken to explore   06 2016 15
the relationship between age and support
for a candidate in an election. The results
of the poll are summarized in the table below.

Age	For	Against	No Opinion
21–40	30	12	8
41–60	20	40	15
Over 60	25	35	15

What percent of the 21-40 age group was
for the candidate?

1)   15   2)   25

3)   40   4)   60

8. The dot plot shown below represents the number of pets owned by students in a class.

    06 2016 20

    Which statement about the data is *not* true?

    1) The median is 3.   2) The interquartile range is 2.

    3) The mean is 3.   4) The data contain no outliers.

9. The two sets of data below represent the number of runs scored by two different youth baseball teams over the course of a season.

    08 2015 19

    Team *A*: 4, 8, 5, 12, 3, 9, 5, 2
    Team *B*: 5, 9, 11, 4, 6, 11, 2, 7

    Which set of statements about the mean and standard deviation is true?

    1) mean A < mean B
        standard deviation A > standard deviation B

    2) mean A > mean B
        standard deviation A < standard deviation B

    3) mean A < mean B
        standard deviation A < standard deviation B

    4) mean A > mean B
        standard deviation A > standard deviation B

10. The table below shows the annual salaries for the 24 members of a professional sports team in terms of millions of dollars.

06 2015 20

0.5	0.5	0.6	0.7	0.75	0.8
1.0	1.0	1.1	1.25	1.3	1.4
1.4	1.8	2.5	3.7	3.8	4
4.2	4.6	5.1	6	6.3	7.2

The team signs an additional player to a contract worth 10 million dollars per year. Which statement about the median and mean is true?

1) Both will increase.

2) Only the median will increase.

3) Only the mean will increase.

4) Neither will change.

11.   Corinne is planning a beach vacation
in July and is analyzing the daily high
temperatures for her potential
destination. She would like to choose
a destination with a high median
temperature and a small interquartile
range. She constructed box plots shown
in the diagram below.

01 2015 14

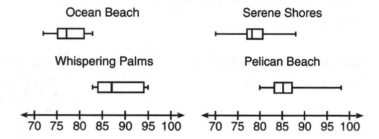

Which destination has a median temperature
above 80 degrees and the smallest
interquartile range?

1)   Ocean Beach

2)   Whispering Palms

3)   Serene Shores

4)   Pelican Beach

NUMBER PROPERTIES

1. A teacher wrote the following set of numbers on the board: 08 2017 25

$$a = \sqrt{20} \quad b = 2.5 \quad c = \sqrt{225}$$

Explain why $a + b$ is irrational, but $b + c$ is rational.

2. State whether $7 - \sqrt{2}$ is rational or irrational. Explain your answer. 06 2017 27

3. A construction worker needs to move 120 ft³ of dirt by using a wheelbarrow. One wheelbarrow load holds 8 ft³ of dirt and each load takes him 10 minutes to complete. One correct way to figure out the number of hours he would need to complete this job is 06 2017 20

1) $\dfrac{120 \text{ ft}^3}{1} \cdot \dfrac{10 \text{ min}}{1 \text{ load}} \cdot \dfrac{60 \text{ min}}{1 \text{ hr}} \cdot \dfrac{1 \text{ load}}{8 \text{ ft}^3}$

2) $\dfrac{120 \text{ ft}^3}{1} \cdot \dfrac{60 \text{ min}}{1 \text{ hr}} \cdot \dfrac{8 \text{ ft}^3}{10 \text{ min}} \cdot \dfrac{1}{1 \text{ load}}$

3) $\dfrac{120 \text{ ft}^3}{1} \cdot \dfrac{1 \text{ load}}{10 \text{ min}} \cdot \dfrac{8 \text{ ft}^3}{1 \text{ load}} \cdot \dfrac{1 \text{ hr}}{60 \text{ min}}$

4) $\dfrac{120 \text{ ft}^3}{1} \cdot \dfrac{1 \text{ load}}{8 \text{ ft}^3} \cdot \dfrac{10 \text{ min}}{1 \text{ load}} \cdot \dfrac{1 \text{ hr}}{60 \text{ min}}$

4. Patricia is trying to compare the average Rainfall of New York to that of Arizona. A comparison between these two states for the months of July through September would be best measured in

08 2016 09

1) feet per hour
2) inches per hour
3) inches per month
4) feet per month

5. Is the sum of $3\sqrt{2}$ and $4\sqrt{2}$ rational or irrational?   Explain your answer.

08 2016 29

6. Dan took 12.5 seconds to run the 100-meter dash. He calculated the time to be approximately

06 2016 08

1) 0.2083 minute
2) 750 minutes
3) 0.2083 hour
4) 0.52083 hour

7. Determine if the product of $3\sqrt{2}$ and $8\sqrt{18}$ is rational or irrational. Explain your answer.

    06 2016 26

8. For which value of *P* and *W* is $P + W$ a rational number?

    08 2015 22

    1) $P = \dfrac{1}{\sqrt{3}}$ and $W = \dfrac{1}{\sqrt{6}}$

    2) $P = \dfrac{1}{\sqrt{4}}$ and $W = \dfrac{1}{\sqrt{9}}$

    3) $P = \dfrac{1}{\sqrt{6}}$ and $W = \dfrac{1}{\sqrt{10}}$

    4) $P = \dfrac{1}{\sqrt{25}}$ and $W = \dfrac{1}{\sqrt{2}}$

9. Which statement is *not* always true?

    06 2015 08

    1) The sum of two rational numbers is rational.

    2) The product of two irrational numbers is rational.

    3 The sum of a rational number and an irrational number is irrational.

    4) The product of a nonzero rational number and an irrational number is irrational.

10. Which domain would be the most appropriate set to use for a function that predicts the number of household online-devices in terms of the number of people in the household?

01 2015 06

   1) integers
   2) whole numbers
   3) irrational numbers
   4) rational numbers

01 2015 25

11. Ms. Fox asked her class "Is the sum of 4.2 and $\sqrt{2}$ rational or irrational?" Patrick answered that the sum would be irrational.

State whether Patrick is correct or incorrect.

Justify your reasoning.

ALGEBRA I

Tuesday, June 12, 2018 — 1:15 to 4:15 p.m., only

The University of the State of New York
REGENTS HIGH SCHOOL EXAMINATION

The possession or use of any communications device is strictly prohibited when taking this examination. If you have or use any communications device, no matter how briefly, your examination will be invalidated and no score will be calculated for you.

A separate answer sheet for **Part I** has been provided to you. Follow the instructions from the proctor for completing the student information on your answer sheet. This examination has four parts, with a total of 37 questions. You must answer all questions in this examination. Record your answers to the Part I multiple-choice questions on the separate answer sheet. Write your answers to the questions in **Parts II, III,** and **IV** directly in this booklet. All work should be written in pen, except for graphs and drawings, which should be done in pencil. Clearly indicate the necessary steps, including appropriate formula substitutions, diagrams, graphs, charts, etc. Utilize the information provided for each question to determine your answer. Note that diagrams are not necessarily drawn to scale. The formulas that you may need to answer some questions in this examination are found at the end of the examination. This sheet is perforated so you may remove it from this booklet. Scrap paper is not permitted for any part of this examination, but you may use the blank spaces in this booklet as scrap paper. A perforated sheet of scrap graph paper is provided at the end of this booklet for any question for which graphing may be helpful but is not required. You may remove this sheet from this booklet. Any work done on this sheet of scrap graph paper will *not* be scored. When you have completed the examination, you must sign the statement printed at the end of the answer sheet, indicating that you had no unlawful knowledge of the questions or answers prior to the examination and that you have neither given nor received assistance in answering any of the questions during the examination. Your answer sheet cannot be accepted if you fail to sign this declaration.

Notice ...
A graphing calculator and a straightedge (ruler) must be available for you to use while taking this examination.

DO NOT OPEN THIS EXAMINATION BOOKLET UNTIL THE SIGNAL IS GIVEN.

Part I
Answer all **24** questions in this part. Each correct answer will receive **2** credits. No partial credit will he allowed. Utilize the information provided for each question to determine your answer. Note that diagrams are not necessarily drawn to scale. For each statement or question, choose the word or expression that, of those given, best completes the statement or answers the question. Record your answers on your separate answer sheet. [48]

1   The solution to $4p + 2 < 2(p + 5)$ is

06 2018 01

    1) $p > -6$ 3) $p > 4$

    2) $p < -6$ 4) $p < 4$

2   If $k(x) = 2x^2 - 3\sqrt{x}$, then $k(9)$ is

06 2018 02

    1)   315   3)   159

    2)   307   4)   153

3   The expression $3(x^2 + 2x - 3) - 4(4x^2 - 7x + 5)$ is equivalent to

06 2018 03

    1) $-13x - 22x + 11$ 3) $19x^2 - 22x + 11$

    2) $-13x^2 + 34x - 29$ 4) $19x^2 + 34x - 29$

4   The zeros of the function $p(x) = x^2 - 2x - 24$ are   06 2018 04

1)   −8 and 3   3)   −4 and 6

2)   −6 and 4   4)   −3 and 8

5   The box plot below summarizes the data for the   06 2018 05
average monthly high temperatures in degrees
Fahrenheit for Orlando, Florida.

The third quartile is

1)   92   3)   83

2)   90   4)   71

6   Joy wants to buy strawberries and   06 2018 06
raspberries to bring to a party. Strawberries
cost $1.60 per pound and raspberries cost
$1.75 per pound. If she only has $10 to spend
on berries, which inequality represents the
situation where she buys x pounds of
strawberries and y pounds of raspberries?

1) $1.60x + 1.75y \le 10$ 3) $1.75x + 1.60y \le 10$

2) $1.60x + 1.75y \ge 10$ 4) $1.75x + 1.60y \ge 10$

7   On the main floor of the Kodak Hall at the
Eastman Theater, the number of seats per row
increases at a constant rate. Steven counts 31
seats in row 3 and 37 seats in row 6.
How many seats are there in row 20?

06 2018 07

1)   65   3)   69

2)   67   4)   71

8   Which ordered pair below is *not* a solution
to $f(x) = x^2 - 3x + 4$?

06 2018 08

1) $(0, 4)$ 3) $(5, 14)$

2) $(1.5, 7.5)$ 4) $(-1, 6)$

9   Students were asked to name their favorite
sport from a list of basketball, soccer, or tennis.
The results are shown in the table below.

06 2018 09

	Basketball	Soccer	Tennis
Girls	42	58	20
Boys	84	41	5

What percentage of the students chose soccer as their
favorite sport?

1)   39.6%   3)   50.4%

2)   41.4%   4)   58.6%

10   The trinomial $x^2 - 14x + 49$ can be expressed as

06 2018 10

1) $(x - 7)^2$ 3) $(x - 7)(x + 7)$

2) $(x + 7)^2$ 4) $(x - 7)(x + 2)$

11   A function is defined as $\{(0, 1), (2, 3), (5, 8), (7, 2)\}$. Isaac is asked to create one more ordered pair for the function. Which ordered pair can he add to the set to keep it a function?

06 2018 11

1) $(0, 2)$ 3) $(7, 0)$

2) $(5, 3)$ 4) $(1, 3)$

12   The quadratic equation $x^2 - 6x = 12$ is rewritten in the form $(x + p)^2 = q$, where q is a constant. What is the value of p?

06 2018 12

1) -12 3) -3

2) -9 4) 9

13 Which of the quadratic functions below has the *smallest* minimum value?

06 2018 13

1) $h(x) = x^2 + 2x - 6$　　　　3) $k(x) = (x + 5)(x + 2)$

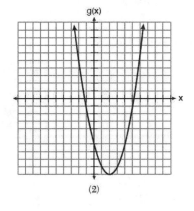

2)　　　(2)

x	f(x)
−1	−2
0	−5
1	−6
2	−5
3	−2

4)

14 Which situation is *not* a linear function?

06 2018 14

1) A gym charges a membership fee of $10.00 down and $10.00 per month.

2) A cab company charges $2.50 initially and $3.00 per mile.

3) A restaurant employee earns $12.50 per hour.

4) A $12,000 car depreciates 15% per year.

15   The Utica Boilermaker is a 15-kilometer road race. Sara is signed up to run this race and has done the following training runs:

06 2018 15

    I.   10 miles
    II.   44,880 feet
    III.   15,560 yards

Which run(s) are at least 15 kilometers?

1)   I, only   3)   I and III

2)   II, only   4)   II and III

16   If $f(x) = x^2 + 2$, which interval describes the range of this function?

06 2018 16

1) $(-\infty, \infty)$ 3) $[2, \infty)$

2) $[0, \infty)$ 4) $(-\infty, 2]$

17   The amount Mike gets paid weekly can be represented by the expression $2.50a + 290$, where a is the number of cell phone accessories he sells that week.
What is the constant term in this expression and what does it represent?

06 2018 17

1) $2.50a$, the amount he is guaranteed to be paid each week

2) $2.50a$, the amount he earns when he sells a accessories

3) 290, the amount he is guaranteed to be paid each week

4) 290, the amount he earns when he sells a accessories

18   A cubic function is graphed on the set of axes below.

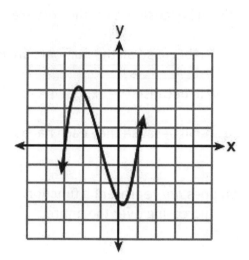

Which function could represent this graph?

1) $f(x) = (x - 3)(x - 1)(x + 1)$
2) $g(x) = (x + 3)(x + 1)(x - 1)$
3) $h(x) = (x - 3)(x - 1)(x + 3)$
4) $k(x) = (x + 3)(x + 1)(x - 3)$

19   Mrs. Allard asked her students to identify which of the polynomials below are in standard form and explain why.

I. $15x^4 - 6x + 3x^2 - 1$

II. $12x^3 + 8x + 4$

III. $2x^5 + 8x^2 + 10x$

Which student's response is correct?

1) Tyler said I and II because the coefficients are decreasing.

2) Susan said only II because all the numbers are decreasing.

3) Fred said II and III because the exponents are decreasing.

4) Alyssa said II and III because they each have three terms.

20   Which graph does *not* represent a function that is always increasing over the entire interval $-2 < x < 2$?

06 2018 20

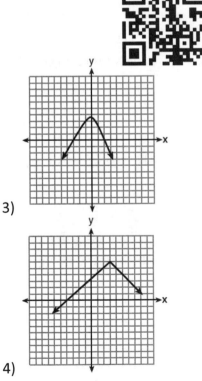

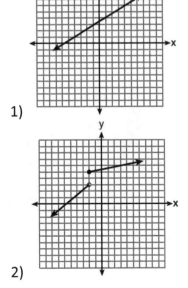

1)

2)

3)

4)

21　At an ice cream shop, the profit, $P(c)$, is modeled by the function $P(c) = 0.87c$, where c represents the number of ice cream cones sold.

06 2018 21

An appropriate domain for this function is

1) an integer ≤ 0　　3) a rational number ≤ 0

2) an integer ≥ 0　　4) a rational number ≥ 0

22　How many real-number solutions does $4x^2 + 2x + 5 = 0$ have?

06 2018 22

1)　one　　　　2)　two

3)　zero　　　　4)　infinitely many

23　Students were asked to write a formula for the length of a rectangle by using the formula for its perimeter, $p = 2\ell + 2w$. Three of their responses are shown below.

06 2018 23

I.　　$\ell = \frac{1}{2}p - w$

II.　　$\ell = \frac{1}{2}(p - 2w)$

III.　　$\ell = \frac{p - 2w}{2}$

Which responses are correct?

1)　I and II, only　　3)　I and III, only

2)　II and III, only　　4)　I, II, and III

24   If $a_n = n(a_{n-1})$ and $a_1 = 1$, what is the value of a_5?

06 2018 24

1)   5   3)   120

2)   20   4)   720

Part II
Answer all 8 questions in this part. Each correct answer will receive 2 credits. Clearly indicate the necessary steps, including appropriate formula substitutions, diagrams, graphs, charts, etc. Utilize the information provided for each question to determine your answer. Note that diagrams are not necessarily drawn to scale. For all questions in this part, a correct numerical answer with no work shown will receive only I credit. All answers should be written in pen, except for graphs and drawings, which should be done in pencil. [16]

25 Graph $f(x) = \sqrt{x+2}$ over the domain $-2 \leq x \leq 7$. 06 2018 25

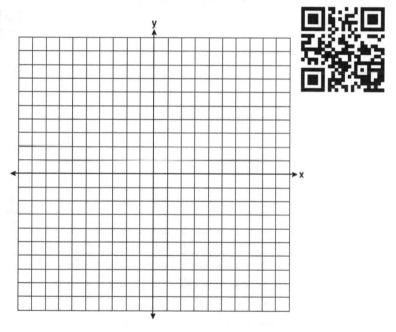

26 Caleb claims that the ordered pairs shown in the table below are from a nonlinear function.

06 2018 26

x	f(x)
0	2
1	4
2	8
3	16

State if Caleb is correct. Explain your reasoning.

27 Solve for *x* to the *nearest tenth*: $x^2 + x - 5 = 0$.

06 2018 27

28 The graph of the function $p(x)$ is represented below. On the same set of axes, sketch the function $p(x + 2)$.

06 2018 28

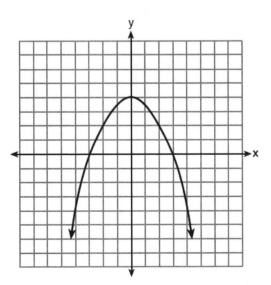

29 When an apple is dropped from a tower 256 feet high, the function $h(t) = -16t^2 + 256$ models the height of the apple, in feet, after t seconds. Determine, algebraically, the number of seconds it takes the apple to hit the ground.

06 2018 29

30 Solve the equation below algebraically for the exact value of x.

$$6 - \frac{2}{3}(x + 5) = 4x$$

06 2018 30

31 Is the product of $\sqrt{16}$ and $\frac{4}{7}$ rational or irrational? Explain your reasoning.

06 2018 31

32   On the set of axes below, graph the piecewise function:

$$f(x) = \begin{cases} -\dfrac{1}{2}x, & x < 2 \\ \\ x, & x \ge 2 \end{cases}$$

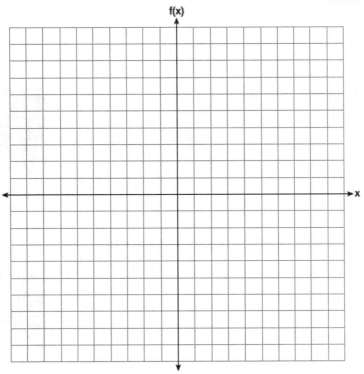

Part III
Answer all 4 questions in this part. Each correct answer will receive 4 credits. Clearly indicate the necessary steps, including appropriate formula substitutions, diagrams, graphs, charts, etc. Utilize the information provided for each question to determine your answer. Note that diagrams are not necessarily drawn to scale. For all questions in this part, a correct numerical answer with no work shown will receive only I credit. All answers should be written in pen, except for graphs and drawings, which should be done in pencil. [16]

33   A population of rabbits in a lab, $p(x)$, can be modeled by the function $p(x) = 20(1.014)^x$, where x represents the number of days since the population was first counted.

06 2018 33

Explain what 20 and 1.014 represent in the context of the problem.

Determine, to the *nearest tenth*, the average rate of change from day 50 to day 100.

34   There are two parking garages in Beacon Falls. Garage *A* charges $7.00 to park for the first 2 hours, and each additional hour costs $3.00. Garage *B* charges $3.25 per hour to park.

06 2018 34

When a person parks for at least 2 hours, write equations to model the cost of parking for a total of *x* hours in Garage *A* and Garage *B*.

Determine algebraically the number of hours when the cost of parking at both garages will be the same.

35 On the set of axes below, graph the following system of inequalities:

$$2y + 3x \le 14$$

$$4x - y < 2$$

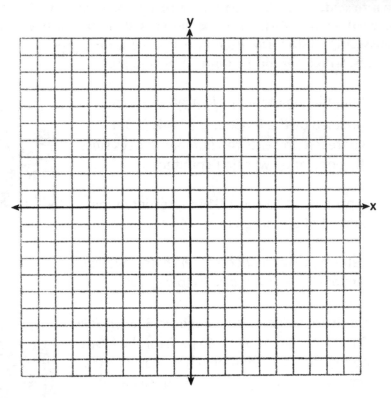

Determine if the point $(1, 2)$ is in the solution set. Explain your answer.

36   The percentage of students scoring 85 or
      better on a mathematics final exam and an
      English final exam during a recent school
      year for seven schools is shown in the
      table   below.

06 2018 36

Percentage of Students Scoring 85 or Better	
Mathematics, x	English, y
27	46
12	28
13	45
10	34
30	56
45	67
20	42

Write the linear regression equation for these data,
rounding all values to the *nearest hundredth*.

State the correlation coefficient of the linear regression
equation, to the *nearest hundredth*.

Explain the meaning of this value in the context
of these data.

Part IV
Answer the question in this part. A correct answer will receive
6 credits. Clearly indicate the necessary steps, including
appropriate formula substitutions, diagrams, graphs, charts,
etc. Utilize the information provided to determine your answer.
Note that diagrams are not necessarily drawn to scale. A correct
numerical answer with no work shown will receive only I credit.
All answers should be written in pen, except for graphs and
drawings, which should be done in pencil. [6]

37   Dylan has a bank that sorts coins as they are   06 2018 37
      dropped into it. A panel on the front displays
      the total number of coins inside as well as the
      total value of these coins. The panel shows 90
      coins with a value of $17.55 inside of the bank.
      If Dylan only collects dimes and quarters, write
      a system of equations in two variables or an
      equation in one variable that could be used to
      model this situation. Using your equation or
      system of equations, algebraically determine the
      number of quarters Dylan has in his bank.
      Dylan's mom told him that she would replace
      each one of his dimes with a quarter. If he uses
      all of his coins, determine if Dylan would then
      have enough money to buy a game priced at
      $20.98 if he must also pay an 8% sales tax.

      Justify your answer.

ALGEBRA I

Thursday, August 16, 2018 - 8:30 to 11:30 a.m., only

The University of the State of New York
REGENTS HIGH SCHOOL EXAMINATION

The possession or use of any communications device is strictly prohibited when taking this examination. If you have or use any communications device, no matter how briefly, your examination will be invalidated and no score will be calculated for you.

A separate answer sheet for **Part I** has been provided to you. Follow the instructions from the proctor for completing the student information on your answer sheet. This examination has four parts, with a total of 37 questions. You must answer all questions in this examination. Record your answers to the Part I multiple-choice questions on the separate answer sheet. Write your answers to the questions in **Parts II, III,** and **IV** directly in this booklet. All work should be written in pen, except for graphs and drawings, which should be done in pencil. Clearly indicate the necessary steps, including appropriate formula substitutions, diagrams, graphs, charts, etc. Utilize the information provided for each question to determine your answer. Note that diagrams are not necessarily drawn to scale. The formulas that you may need to answer some questions in this examination are found at the end of the examination. This sheet is perforated so you may remove it from this booklet. Scrap paper is not permitted for any part of this examination, but you may use the blank spaces in this booklet as scrap paper. A perforated sheet of scrap graph paper is provided at the end of this booklet for any question for which graphing may be helpful but is not required. You may remove this sheet from this booklet. Any work done on this sheet of scrap graph paper will *not* be scored. When you have completed the examination, you must sign the statement printed at the end of the answer sheet, indicating that you had no unlawful knowledge of the questions or answers prior to the examination and that you have neither given nor received assistance in answering any of the questions during the examination. Your answer sheet cannot be accepted if you fail to sign this declaration.

Notice …
A graphing calculator and a straightedge (ruler) must be available for you to use while taking this examination.

DO NOT OPEN THIS EXAMINATION BOOKLET UNTIL THE SIGNAL IS GIVEN.

Part I
Answer all 24 questions in this part. Each correct answer will receive 2 credits. No partial credit will he allowed. Utilize the information provided for each question to determine your answer. Note that diagrams are not necessarily drawn to scale. For each statement or question, choose the word or expression that, of those given, best completes the statement or answers the question. Record your answers on your separate answer sheet. [48]

1. The number of bacteria grown in a lab can be modeled by $P(t) = 300 \cdot 2^{4t}$, where t is the number of hours. Which expression is equivalent to $P(t)$?

   08 2018 01

   (1) $300 \cdot 8^t$ (3) $300^t \cdot 2^4$

   (2) $300 \cdot 16^t$ (4) $300^{2t} \cdot 2^{2t}$

2. During physical education class, Andrew recorded the exercise times in minutes and heart rates in beats per minute (bpm) of four of his classmates. Which table best represents a linear model of exercise time and heart rate?

   08 2018 02

Student 1	
Exercise Time (in minutes)	**Heart Rate** (bpm)
0	60
1	65
2	70
3	75
4	80

(1)

Student 3	
Exercise Time (in minutes)	**Heart Rate** (bpm)
0	58
1	65
2	70
3	75
4	79

(3)

Student 2	
Exercise Time (in minutes)	**Heart Rate** (bpm)
0	62
1	70
2	83
3	88
4	90

(2)

Student 4	
Exercise Time (in minutes)	**Heart Rate** (bpm)
0	62
1	65
2	66
3	73
4	75

(4)

3. David correctly factored the expression $m^2 - 12m - 64$.

08 2018 03

Which expression did he write?

(1) $(m - 8)(m - 8)$ (3) $(m - 16)(m + 4)$

(2) $(m - 8)(m + 8)$ (4) $(m + 16)(m - 4)$

4. The solution to $-2(1 - 4x) = 3x + 8$ is

08 2018 04

(1) $\frac{6}{11}$ (3) $-\frac{10}{7}$

(2) 2   (4) -2

155

5. The graph of $f(x)$ is shown below.

08 2018 05

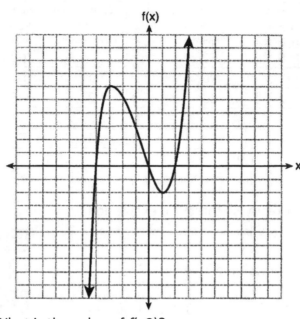

What is the value of $f(-3)$?

(1) 6   (3) –2

(2) 2   (4) –4

6. If the function $f(x) = x^2$ has the domain $\{0, 1, 4, 9\}$, what is its range?

08 2018 06

(1) {0, 1, 2, 3}

(2) {0, 1, 16, 81}

(3) {0, –1, 1, –2, 2, –3, 3}

(4) {0, –1, 1, –16, 16, –81, 81}

7. The expression $4x^2 - 25$ is equivalent to

(1) $(4x - 5)(x + 5)$ (3) $(2x + 5)(2x - 5)$

(2) $(4x + 5)(x - 5)$ (4) $(2x - 5)(2x - 5)$

8. Compared to the graph of $f(x) = x^2$, the graph of $g(x) = (x - 2)^2 + 3$ is the result of translating $f(x)$

(1) 2 units up and 3 units right
(2) 2 units down and 3 units up
(3) 2 units right and 3 units up
(4) 2 units left and 3 units right

9. Lizzy has 30 coins that total $4.80. All of her coins are dimes, *D*, and quarters, *Q*. Which system of equations models this situation?

(1) $D + Q = 4.80$ (3) $D + Q = 30$
    $.10D + .25Q = 30$ $.25D + .10Q = 4.80$

(2) $D + Q = 30$ (4) $D + Q = 4.80$
    $.10D + .25Q = 4.80$ $.25D + .10Q = 30$

10. Gretchen has $50 that she can spend at the fair. Ride tickets cost $1.25 each and game tickets cost $2 each. She wants to go on a minimum of 10 rides and play at least 12 games. Which system of inequalities represents this situation when *r* is the number of ride tickets purchased and *g* is the number of game tickets purchased?

08 2018 10

(1)　1.25r + 2g < 50
　　　r ≤ 10
　　　g > 12

(3) 1.25r + 2g ≤ 50
　　r ≥ 10
　　g > 12

(2)　1.25r + 2g ≤ 50
　　　r ≥ 10
　　　g ≥ 12

(4) 1.25r + 2g < 50
　　r ≤ 10
　　g ≥ 12

11. Three functions are shown below.

08 2018 11

f(x)

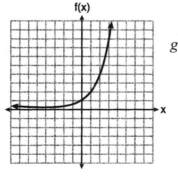

$g(x) = 3^x + 2$

x	h(x)
−5	30
−4	14
−3	6
−2	2
−1	0
0	−1
1	−1.5
2	−1.75

Which statement is true?

(1) The *y*–intercept for *h*(*x*) is greater than the *y*–intercept for *f*(*x*).

(2) The *y*–intercept for *f*(*x*) is greater than the *y*–intercept for *g*(*x*).

(3) The *y*–intercept for *h*(*x*) is greater than the *y*–intercept for both *g*(*x*) and *f*(*x*).

(4) The *y*–intercept for *g*(*x*) is greater than the *y*–intercept for both *f*(*x*) and *h*(*x*).

12. Olivia entered a baking contest. As part of the contest, she needs to demonstrate how to measure a gallon of milk if she only has a teaspoon measure. She converts the measurement using the ratios below:

08 2018 12

$$\frac{4\ quarts}{1\ gallon} \bullet \frac{2\ pints}{1\ quart} \bullet \frac{2\ cups}{1\ pint} \bullet \frac{\frac{1}{4}\ cup}{4\ tablespoons} \bullet \frac{3\ teaspoons}{1\ tablespoon}$$

Which ratio is *incorrectly* written in Olivia's conversion?

(1) $\dfrac{4\ quarts}{1\ gallon}$

(2) $\dfrac{2\ pints}{1\ quart}$

(3) $\dfrac{\frac{1}{4}\ cup}{4\ tablespoons}$

(4) $\dfrac{3\ teaspoons}{1\ tablespoon}$

13. If $y = 3x^3 + x^2 - 5$ and $z = x^2 - 12$, which polynomial is equivalent to $2(y + z)$?

08 2018 13

(1) $6x^3 + 4x^2 - 34$ (3) $6x^3 + 3x^2 - 22$

(2) $6x^3 + 3x^2 - 17$ (4) $6x^3 + 2x^2 - 17$

14. An outdoor club conducted a survey of its members. The members were asked to state their preference between skiing and snowboarding. Each member had to pick one. Of the 60 males, 45 stated they preferred to snowboard. Twenty–two of the 60 females preferred to ski. What is the relative frequency that a male prefers to ski?

08 2018 14

(1) 0.125   (3) $0.\overline{333}$

(2) 0.25   (4) $0.\overline{405}$

15. When the function $g(x) \begin{cases} 5x, x \le 3 \\ x^2 + 4, x > 3 \end{cases}$ is graphed correctly, how should the points be drawn on the graph for an x–value of 3?

08 2018 15

(1) open circles at (3,15) and (3,13)
(2) closed circles at (3,15) and (3,13)
(3) an open circle at (3,15) and a closed circle at (3,13)
(4) a closed circle at (3,15) and an open circle at (3,13)

16. If $f(x) = 2x^2 + x - 3$, which equation can be used to determine the zeros of the function?

(1) $0 = (2x - 3)(x + 1)$ (3) $0 = 2x(x + 1) - 3$

(2) $0 = (2x + 3)(x - 1)$ (4) $0 = 2x(x - 1) - 3(x + 1)$

17. Each day, a local dog shelter spends an average of $2.40 on food per dog. The manager estimates the shelter's daily expenses, assuming there is at least one dog in the shelter, using the function $E(x) = 30 + 2.40x$.

Which statements regarding the function $E(x)$ are correct?

I. x represents the number of dogs at the shelter per day.
II. x represents the number of volunteers at the shelter per day.
III. 30 represents the shelter's total expenses per day.
IV. 30 represents the shelter's nonfood expenses per day.

(1) I and III   (3) II and III

(2) I and IV   (4) II and IV

18. Which point is not in the solution set of the equation $3y + 2 = x^2 - 5x + 17$?

(1) $(-2,10)$ (3) $(2,3)$

(2) $(-1,7)$ (4) $(5,5)$

19. The functions *f(x)* and *g(x)* are graphed below.

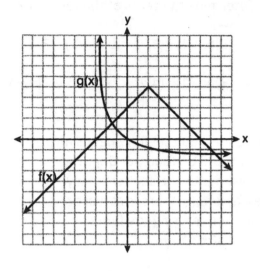

Based on the graph, the solutions to the equation $f(x) = g(x)$ are

(1) the *x*–intercepts
(2) the *y*–intercepts
(3) the *x*–values of the points of intersection
4) the *y*–values of the points of intersection

20. For the sequence –27, –12, 3, 18, ... , the expression that defines the *n*th term where $a_1 = -27$ is

(1) $15 - 27n$ (3) $-27 + 15n$

(2) $15 - 27(n - 1)$ (4) $-27 + 15(n - 1)$

21. The data obtained from a random sample of track athletes showed that as the foot size of the athlete decreased, the average running speed decreased. Which statement is best supported by the data?

08 2018 21

(1) Smaller foot sizes cause track athletes to run slower.

(2) The sample of track athletes shows a causal relationship between foot size and running speed.

(3) The sample of track athletes shows a correlation between foot size and running speed.

(4) There is no correlation between foot size and running speed in track athletes.

22. Which system of equations will yield the same solution as the system below?

08 2018 22

$$x - y = 3$$
$$2x - 3y = -1$$

(1) $-2x - 2y = -6$
    $2x - 3y = -1$

(3) $2x - 2y = 6$
    $2x - 3y = -1$

(2) $-2x + 2y = 3$
    $2x - 3y = -1$

(4) $3x + 3y = 9$
    $2x - 3y = -1$

23. Which of the three situations given below is best modeled by an exponential function?

I.   A bacteria culture doubles in size every day.
II. A plant grows by 1 inch every 4 days.
III. The population of a town declines by 5% every 3 years.

(1) I, only   (3) I and II

(2) II, only   (4) I and III

24. The length, width, and height of a rectangular box are represented by $2x$, $3x + 1$, and $5x - 6$, respectively. When the volume is expressed as a polynomial in standard form, what is the coefficient of the 2nd term?

(1) –13   (3) –26

(2) 13   (4) 26

Part II

Answer all 8 questions in this part. Each correct answer will receive 2 credits. Clearly indicate the necessary steps, including appropriate formula substitutions, diagrams, graphs, charts, etc. Utilize the information provided for each question to determine your answer. Note that diagrams are not necessarily drawn to scale. For all questions in this part, a correct numerical answer with no work shown will receive only I credit. All answers should be written in pen, except for graphs and drawings, which should be done in pencil. [16]

25. Explain how to determine the zeros of $f(x) = (x + 3)(x - I)(x - 8)$.

   State the zeros of the function.

08 2018 25

26. Four relations are shown below.

08 2018 26

x	y
− 4	1
0	3
4	5
6	6

I

III

$\{(1, 2), (2, 5), (3, 8), (2, - 5), (1, - 2)\}$

$y = x^2$

II

IV

State which relation(s) are functions.
Explain why the other relation(s) are *not* functions.

27. The table below represents the height of a bird above the ground during flight, with *P(t)* representing height in feet and *t* representing time in seconds.

08 2018 27

t	P(t)
0	6.71
3	6.26
4	6
9	3.41

Calculate the average rate of change from 3 to 9 seconds, in feet per second.

28. Is the solution to the quadratic equation written below rational or irrational? Justify your answer.

08 2018 28

$$0 = 2x^2 + 3x - 10$$

29. The formula for converting degrees Fahrenheit (*F*) to degrees Kelvin (*K*) is:

08 2018 29

$$K = \frac{5}{9}(F + 459.67)$$

Solve for *F*, in terms of *K*.

30. Solve the following equation by completing the square:

$$x^2 + 4x = 2$$

31. The students in Mrs. Lankford's 4th and 6th period Algebra classes took the same test. The results of the scores are shown in the following table:

	$\overline{x}$	σ_x	n	min	Q_1	med	Q_3	max
4th Period	77.75	10.79	20	58	69	76.5	87.5	96
6th Period	78.4	9.83	20	59	71.5	78	88	96

Based on these data, which class has the largest spread of test scores? Explain how you arrived at your answer.

32. Write the first five terms of the recursive sequence defined below.

$a_1 = 0$
$a_n = 2(a_{n-1})^2 - 1$, for $n > 1$

Part III
Answer all 4 questions in this part. Each correct answer will receive 4 credits. Clearly indicate the necessary steps, including appropriate formula substitutions, diagrams, graphs, charts, etc. Utilize the information provided for each question to determine your answer. Note that diagrams are not necessarily drawn to scale. For all questions in this part, a correct numerical answer with no work shown will receive only I credit. All answers should be written in pen, except for graphs and drawings, which should be done in pencil. [16]

33. Sarah wants to buy a snowboard that has a total cost of $580, including tax. She has already saved $135 for it. At the end of each week, she is paid $96 for babysitting and is going to save three-quarters of that for the snowboard.

08 2018 33

Write an inequality that can be used to determine the *minimum* number of weeks Sarah needs to babysit to have enough money to purchase the snowboard.

Determine and state the *minimum* number of full weeks Sarah needs to babysit to have enough money to purchase this snowboard.

34. A car was purchased for $25,000. Research shows that the car has an average yearly depreciation rate of 18.5%.

08 2018 34

Create a function that will determine the value, *V(t)*, of the car *t* years after purchase.

Determine, to the *nearest cent,* how much the car will depreciate from year 3 to year 4.

35. Graph the following system of inequalities on the set of axes below:

$$2y \geq 3x - 16$$
$$y + 2x > -5$$

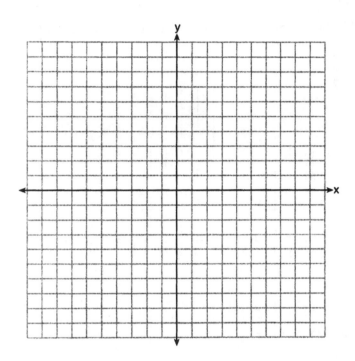

Based upon your graph, explain why (6,1) is a solution to this system and why (− 6,7) is *not* a solution to this system.

36. Paul plans to have a rectangular garden adjacent to his garage. He will use 36 feet of fence to enclose three sides of the garden. The area of the garden, in square feet, can be modeled by $f(w) = w(36 - 2w)$, where w is the width in feet.

08 2018 36

On the set of axes below, sketch the graph of $f(w)$.

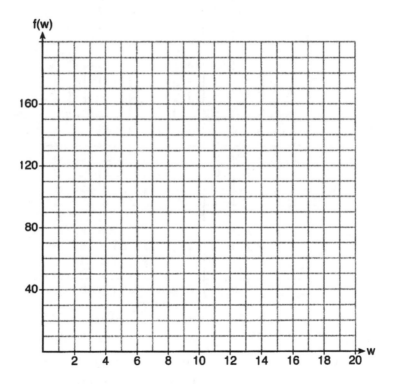

Explain the meaning of the vertex in the context of the problem.

Part IV
Answer the question in this part. A correct answer will receive
6 credits. Clearly indicate the necessary steps, including
appropriate formula substitutions, diagrams, graphs, charts,
etc. Utilize the information provided to determine your answer.
Note that diagrams are not necessarily drawn to scale. A correct
numerical answer with no work shown will receive only I credit.
All answers should be written in pen, except for graphs and
drawings, which should be done in pencil. [6]

37. At the present time, Mrs. Bee's age is six years
more than four times her son's age. Three
years ago, she was seven times as old as her
son was then.

08 2018 37

If *b* represents Mrs. Bee's age now and
s represents her son's age now, write a
system of equations that could be used
to model this scenario.

Use this system of equations to determine,
algebraically, the ages of both Mrs. Bee and
her son now.

Determine how many years from now Mrs. Bee
will be three times as old as her son will be then.

Accepted Solutions and Point Allocation

Polynomials

1. [2] $8x^3 + 22x^2 - 4x$, and correct work is shown.
2. [2] 1
3. [4] –6 and 3, and correct work is shown, and a correct explanation is written.
4. [2] 0 and 1, and correct work is shown.
5. [2] $5x^2 - 10$ or $5(x^2 - 2)$, and appropriate work is shown.
6. [2] 3
7. [2] 1
8. [2] 3
9. [2] No, and a correct explanation is written.
10. [2] 3
11. [2] 4
12. [2] 2
13. [2] 3
14. [2] 4
15. [2] $x^4 - \frac{5}{2}x^3 + \frac{7}{2}x^2$, and correct work is shown.
16. [2] 2
17. [2] $-2x^2 + 6x + 4$ or equivalent trinomial, and correct work is shown.

Properties of Algebra

1. [2] 46, and correct work is shown.
2. [2] $r = \sqrt{\dfrac{3V}{\pi h}}$, and correct work is shown.
3. [2] 2
4. [2] 4
5. [2] 3
6. [2] 1
7. [2] 2
8. [2] $\dfrac{13+3a}{a}$ *or* $\dfrac{13}{a} + 3$ is written, and correct work is shown.
9. [2] $n = \dfrac{S+360}{180}$ *or* $n = \dfrac{S}{180} + 2$ and correct work is shown.
10. [4] $r = \sqrt{\dfrac{V}{\pi h}}$ and 5, and correct work is shown.
11. [2] 2
12. [2] 1
13. [2] 2
14. [2] 1
15. [2] 1
16. [2] 25, and correct work is shown.

Functions

1. [2] 3
2. [2] 1
3. [2] 1
4. [2] 2
5. [2] 3
6. [2] 2
7. [4] 3.6 and –3.1, and correct algebraic work is shown, and a correct explanation is written.
8. [2] $f(x)$ is shifted right by a and $f(x)$ is shifted down by a are stated.
9. [2] 1
10. [2] 3
11. [2] 3
12. [2] 3
13. [2] 1

14. [2] 4
15. [2] 2
16. [2] 4
17. [2] 1
18. [2] 2
19. [2] A correct description is written.
20. [2] −3 and 1 are stated.
21. [2] 1
22. [2] 1
23. [2] 2
24. [2] 1
25. [2] 4
26. [2] $2(2x +1)^2 - 1$ or an equivalent expression is written.
27. [2] $g(x) = x^3 + 2x^2 - 4$ or $g(x) = f(x) - 4$, and a correct explanation is written.
28. [2] 1
29. [2] 2
30. [2] 3
31. [2] 3
32. [2] 4
33. [2] 1
34. [4] 200, and correct work is shown, 43 and a correct explanation is given.
35. [2] (− 4,1), and a correct explanation is given.
36. [2] A correct graph is drawn.

Creating and Interpreting Equations

1. [6] $1.25x + 2.50y + 3.50 = 28.50$ or an equivalent equation, a correct graph is drawn, 11 is stated, and a correct explanation is given.
2. [4] 10 and 0.3, and correct work is shown.
3. [2] 4
4. [2] 4
5. [2] 15, and a correct justification is written.
6. [2] 2
7. [2] 3
8. [2] 3
9. [2] 2
10. [2] A correct justification is given.
11. [2] The number of inches of snow falling per hour or an equivalent explanation is written.
12. [4] 9.5, $y = 9.5x$ and 1028, and correct work is shown.
13. [2] 3
14. [2] 4
15. [2] 4
16. [2] 1
17. [2] 3
18. [2] 2
19. [2] A correct function is written, such as $f(x) = 6.50x + 4(12)$.
20. [2] 619.35, and correct work is shown.
21. [2] 2
22. [2] 4
23. [2] 12/5 or 2.4, and correct algebraic work is shown.
24. [6] $(x - 3)(2x) = 1.25x^2$ or an equivalent quadratic in one variable is written, a correct explanation is written, 80, and correct work is shown.

Inequalities

1. [4] Both inequalities are graphed correctly and at least one is labeled, the solution is labeled *S*, and a correct explanation indicating a negative response is written.
2. [2] 1
3. [2] The inequality is graphed and shaded correctly.
4. [2] 4
5. [2] 1
6. [2] 1
7. [4] A correct explanation is written and a correct graph is drawn.
8. [2] 2
9. [2] 4
10. [2] 3
11. [2] 4
12. [2] 3
13. [2] The inequality is graphed correctly.
14. [4] $x \geq 6$, and correct algebraic work is shown. 6, 7, and 8, and a correct explanation is written.
15. [2] 1
16. [2] 4
17. [2] 0, and correct work is shown.
18. [4] A correct system of inequalities is graphed and at least one inequality is labeled. A correct combination is stated, and a correct explanation is given.
19. [2] 1
20. [2] 3
21. [4] $y \geq 2x - 3$, a correct graph, and disagree, and a correct explanation is written.

Sequences and Series

1.   [2] A correct explanation indicating a positive response is written.
2.   [2] 3
3.   [2] 2
4.   [2] 1
5.   [2] 3
6.   [2] 1
7.   [2] 3
8.   [2] $h(n) = 1.5(n - 1) + 3$ or an equivalent equation is written.
9.   [2] $T(d) = 30 + 2(d - 1)$ or an equivalent equation and 40 are written
10.   [2] 3
11.   [2] 3

Systems of Equations

1.   [2] Two correct explanations are written.
2.   [2] 4
3.   [6] $y = 10x + 5$ and $y = 5x + 35$ are written and graphed correctly, and at least one is labeled, and a correct explanation is written.
4.   [2] 1
5.   [2] 4
6.   [4] A correct system of inequalities is written, 48, and a correct justification is given.
7.   [6] $18j + 32w = 19.92$ and $14j + 26w = 15.76$, a correct justification is given, and correct work is shown to find j = 0.68 and w = 0.24.
8.   [2] 1
9.   [2] 4
10.   [2] 2
11.   [4] Both inequalities are graphed correctly and at least one is labeled, and a correct explanation stating he is incorrect is written.

12. [6] 3x + 2y = 19 and 2x + 4y = 24 are written and graphed correctly, and at least one is labeled, x = 3.50 and y = 4.25 or the coordinates (3.50, 4.25) are stated, and a justification is given.
13. [2] 2
14. [2] 3
15. [4] Agree (or yes), and a correct justification is given.
16. [2] 3
17. [4] A correct system of equations is written, popcorn = 5.75, drink = 2.25 and correct work is shown.

Quadratic Equations and Factoring

1. [4] (4, 9256), and a correct explanation is written, and 256, and a correct justification is given.
2. [2] $3 \pm \sqrt{24}$ *or* $3 \pm 2\sqrt{6}$, and correct work is shown.
3. [2] 3
4. [2] 3
5. [2] 2
6. [2] 3
7. [2] 2
8. [2] 3
9. [2] 1
10. [2] 3
11. [2] –4 and 10, and correct algebraic work is shown.
12. [4] $-\frac{3}{8}$ *and* $\frac{1}{8}$ or equivalent, correct work is shown, and a correct explanation is written.
13. [2] 3
14. [2] 3
15. [2] Yes, and a correct explanation is written.
16. [4] 48, 3, and correct work is shown.
17. [2] 4
18. [2] 2
19. [2] 1
20. [2] 3
21. [2] None, and a correct justification is given.
22. [2] $0 \leq t \leq 4$ or equivalent, and a correct explanation is written.

23. [6] A correct equation or inequality is written, a correct explanation is written, 1.5, and correct work is shown.
24. [2] 2
25. [2] 4
26. [2] 3
27. [2] 4
28. [2] 1
29. [2] 7, and a correct explanation is given.
30. [2] A correct equation is written, 4.1, and correct work is shown.
31. [6] A correct graph is drawn, (75, 25) is stated and interpreted, no, and a correct justification is given.
32. [2] 4
33. [2] 4
34. [2] 3
35. [2] 1
36. [2] 7/2 and −1/ 2 , and correct algebraic work is shown.
37. [4] Maximum is stated, a correct explanation is written, and $f(x) = -(x-4)^2 + 25$, and correct work is shown using completing the square.

Regression

1. [2] 1
2. [2] 1
3. [2] 2
4. [4] y = 17.159x − 2.476 and 8.7, and correct work is shown.
5. [2] 2
6. [4] $y = 0.16x + 8.27$, 0.97, and a strong association are stated.
7. [2] 2
8. [2] Graph A, and a correct explanation is written.
9. [4] 0.94 and a correct explanation is written.

Exponential Equations

1.   [2] 3
2.   [2] 2
3.   [2] 2
4.   [4] $f(x) = 10 + 100x$ and $g(x) = 10(2)^x$ or equivalent functions, "both" is stated, and a correct justification is given.
5.   [2] 2
6.   [2] 1
7.   [2] 1
8.   [2] 2
9.   [2] Exponential, and a correct explanation is written.
10.   [2] 3
11.   [2] 2
12   [2] 3
13.   [2] Marc or exponential, and a correct explanation is written.
14.   [2] 5, and a correct explanation is written.
15.   [4] Both graphs are drawn correctly, $g(x)$ is stated, and a correct justification is given.
16.   [2] 2
17.   [4] $y = 80(1.5)^x$, or an equivalent equation, 3,030,140, no, and correct work is shown and a correct explanation is given.
18.   [2] 1
19.   [2] 1
20.   [2] 3
21.   [2] 4
22.   [2] $y = 0.25(2)^x$ or an equivalent equation is written, and a correct explanation is given.

Graphing

1. [2] A correct explanation indicating a positive response is written.
2. [2] 3
3. [2] 2
4. [2] 1
5. [4] D to E with a correct explanation is written, a correct explanation for interval B to C is written, and 32.9.
6. [2] A correct graph is drawn and $(-3,9)$ is stated.
7. [2] 4
8. [2] 4
9. [2] 3
10. [2] 3
11. [2] 4
12. [2] 1
13. [2] A correct graph is drawn.
14. [2] A correct graph is drawn and x = 2 is stated.
15. [4] Correct graphs are drawn, 1, and a correct explanation is written.
16. [2] 2
17. [2] 2
18. [2] 4
19. [2] A correct graph is drawn.
20. [2] 4
21. [2] 1
22. [2] 3
23. [2] 2
24. [2] A correct graph is drawn, and a correct explanation is written.
25. [2] 3
26. [2] 4
27. [2] 4
28. [2] 2
29. [4] Maximum is stated, a correct explanation is written, and $f(x) = -(x-4)^2 + 25$, and correct work is shown using completing the square.

Statistics

1. [4] A correct table is completed, a correct histogram is drawn, 6.4 – 6.5, and a correct justification is given.
2. [2] 2
3. [2] 2
4. [2] The frequency table is completed correctly.
5. [2] 4
6. [2] 4
7. [2] 4
8. [2] 3
9. [2] 1
10. [2] 3
11. [2] 4

Number Properties

1. [2] Two correct explanations are written.
2. [2] Irrational, and a correct explanation is written.
3. [2] 4
4. [2] 3
5. [2] Irrational, and a correct explanation is written.
6. [2] 1
7. [2] Rational, and a correct explanation is written.
8. [2] 2
9. [2] 2
10. [2] 2
11. [2] Correct is stated and a correct justification is given.

ALGEBRA I

Tuesday, June 12, 2018 — 1:15 to 4:15 p.m., only

Part I

Allow a total of 48 credits, 2 credits for each of the following.

(1) . . . . . 4 . . . . .   (2) . . . . . 4 . . . . .   (3) . . . . . 2 . . . . .

(4) . . . . . 3 . . . . .   (5) . . . . . 2 . . . . .   (6) . . . . . 1 . . . . .

(7) . . . . . 1 . . . . .   (8) . . . . . 4 . . . . .   (9) . . . . . 1 . . . . .

(10) . . . . . 1 . . . . .   (11) . . . . . 4 . . . . .   (12) . . . . 3 . . . . .

(13) . . . . . 2 . . . . .   (14) . . . . . 4 . . . . .   (15) . . . . 1 . . . . .

(16) . . . . . 3 . . . . .   (17) . . . . . 3 . . . . .   (18) . . . . 2 . . . . .

(19) . . . . . 3 . . . . .   (20) . . . . . 3 . . . . .   (21) . . . . 2 . . . . .

(22) . . . . . 3 . . . . .   (23) . . . . . 4 . . . . .   (24) . . . . 3 . . . . .

Part II

For each question, use the specific criteria to award a maximum of 2 credits. Unless otherwise specified, mathematically correct alternative solutions should be awarded appropriate credit.

(25) **[2]** A correct graph is drawn over the given domain.

(26) **[2]** A correct explanation indicating a positive response is written.

(27) **[2]** 1.8 and –2.8, and correct work is shown.

(28) **[2]** A correct graph is drawn.

(29) **[2]** 4, and correct algebraic work is shown.

(30) **[2]** $\frac{8}{14}$ or $0.\overline{571428}$, or an equivalent fraction, and correct work is shown.

(31) **[2]** Rational is stated, and a correct explanation is written.

(32) **[2]** A correct graph is drawn.

Part III

For each question, use the specific criteria to award a maximum of 4 credits. Unless otherwise specified, mathematically correct alternative solutions should be awarded appropriate credit.

(33) **[4]** Correct explanations are written, 0.8, and correct work is shown.

(34) **[4]** Correct equations are written, and 4, and correct algebraic work is shown.

(35) **[4]** The system of inequalities is graphed correctly and at least one is labeled, and a correct explanation indicating a negative response is written.

(36) **[4]** $y = 0.96x + 23.95$, 0.92, and a correct explanation in context is written.

Part IV

For this question, use the specific criteria to award a maximum of 6 credits. Unless otherwise specified, mathematically correct alternative solutions should be awarded appropriate credit.

(37) **[6]** $d + q = 90$, $.10d + .25q = 17.55$ or an equivalent system, or an equation in one variable, 57, and correct algebraic work is shown, and a correct justification indicating that Dylan won't have enough money is written.

ALGEBRA I

Thursday, August 16, 2018 — 8:30 to 11:30 a.m., only

Part I

Allow a total of 48 credits, 2 credits for each of the following.

(1) . . . . . 2 . . . . .   (2) . . . . . 1 . . . . .   (3) . . . . . 3 . . . . .

(4) . . . . . 2 . . . . .   (5) . . . . . 1 . . . . .   (6) . . . . . 2 . . . . .

(7) . . . . . 3. . . . .   (8) . . . . 3 . . . . .   (9) . . . . . 2 . . . . .

(10) . . . . .2 . . . . .   (11) . . . . 4 . . . . .   (12) . . . . .3 . . . . .

(13) . . . . .1 . . . .   (14) . . . . . 2 . . . . .   (15) . . . . .4 . . . . .

(16) . . . . .2 . . . . .   (17) . . . . 2 . . . . .   (18) . . . . .1 . . . . .

(19) . . . . . 3 . . . . .   (20) . . . . 4 . . . . .   (21) . . . . . 3 . . . . .

(22) . . . . . 3 . . . . .   (23) . . . . . 4 . . . . .   (24) . . . . . 3 . . . . .

Part II

For each question, use the specific criteria to award a maximum of 2 credits. Unless otherwise specified, mathematically correct alternative solutions should be awarded appropriate credit.

(25) **[2]** A correct explanation is written, and –3, 1, and 8 are stated.

(26) **[2]** III and IV are stated, and a correct explanation is written.

(27) **[2]** –0.475 is stated, and correct work is shown.

(28) **[2]** Irrational, and a correct justification is given.

(29) **[2]** $F = \frac{9}{5}K - 459.67$ or equivalent equation is written, and correct work is shown.

(30) **[2]** $-2 \pm \sqrt{6}$, and correct work using the method of completing the square is shown.

(31) **[2]** 4th, and a correct explanation is written.

(32) **[2]** 0, –1, 1, 1, 1.

Part III

For each question, use the specific criteria to award a maximum of 4 credits. Unless otherwise specified, mathematically correct alternative solutions should be awarded appropriate credit.

(33) **[4]** $135 + 72x \geq 580$ or an equivalent inequality, and 7, and correct work is shown.

(34) **[4]** $V(t) = 25,000(1 - 0.185)^t$ or $V(t) = 25,000(0.815)^t$, and 2503.71, and correct work is shown.

(35) **[4]** The system of inequalities is graphed correctly, and at least one is labeled, and explanations for both points are written.

(36) **[4]** A correct sketch is drawn, and a correct explanation in context is written.

Part IV

For this question, use the specific criteria to award a maximum of 6 credits. Unless otherwise specified, mathematically correct alternative solutions should be awarded appropriate credit.

(37) **[6]** A correct system of equations is written, correct algebraic work is shown to find 38 and 8, and correct work is shown to find 7.